GAMEBIRDS OF THE
NORTHERN HEMISPHERE

GAMEBIRDS OF THE NORTHERN HEMISPHERE

by

IAIN BRODIE

Published by:
Whitewolf Publications
Aviemore, Inverness-shire, Scotland

© IAIN BRODIE

ISBN 0 948178 00 0

Typesetting by:
Pacesetter Typesetting, Portsmouth, Hampshire

Printed by:
J. G. Eccles, Inverness, Scotland

CONTENTS

		Page
List of Illustrations		vi
Acknowledgements		vii
Introduction		1

Chapters

1	Evolution of Gallinaceous Gamebirds	3
2	Conservation of Gamebirds	13
2.1	Conservation and Aviculture	21
2.2	International Controls and Licensing of Endangered Species	29
3	Ornithological Descriptions	37
3.1	Tetraonidae I *(The Grouse)*	38
3.2	Tetraonidae II *(The Snowcocks)*	83
3.3	Tetraonidae III *(The Pheasant Grouse)*	86
3.4	Phasianidae I *(The Pheasants)*	88
3.5	Phasianidae II *(The Partridges and Francolins)*	117
3.6	Phasianidae III *(The Quail)*	133
3.7	Meleagrididae *(The Turkeys)*	148
4	Gamebirds in Aviculture	153
4.1	Aviary Planning and Construction	158
4.2	Aviary Plants and Shrubs	170
4.3	Incubation Techniques and Procedure	179
4.4	Rearing and Feeding	194
4.5	Artificial Propagation of Gamebirds for Hunting	206
4.6	Hygiene and Veterinary Care in Captivity	215
Appendix I		223
Appendix II		231
Index of Common Names		233
Index of Scientific Names		237

LIST OF ILLUSTRATIONS

		Page
Figure 1	Evolutionary Distribution Map	4
Figure 2	Evolutionary Family Tree	6
Figure 3	Quail Hybrids (after Johnsgard)	8
Figure 4	Habitat Zones	17
Figure 5	Vulnerability Factor	19
Figure 6	Light and Seclusion Pen	26
Figure 7	Transport Box for Birds	36
Figure 8	Aviary Layout	162
Figure 9	Diagram of Developing Embryo	182
Figure 10	Diagram of Trays	191
Figure 11	Brooder Layout and Siting	196
Figure 12	Artificial Propagation of Gamebirds	207
Figure 13	Laying Pen for Partridges	211
Figure 14	Laying Pen for Quail	212
Figure 15	Laying Pen for Grouse	213
Figure 16	Laying Pen for Pheasant	214

Acknowledgements

One of the great difficulties that any Author who has received so much help, encouragement and advice, from some of the most generous and kind people I have so far had the pleasure to meet or am ever likely to, is that it proves very hard to mention everyone by name.

Nevertheless, some very significant help was given and I would like to acknowledge several of these kind people, specifically: –

Dr. Wolfgang Scherzinger, Dr. H. Aschenbrenner, Professor E. Pulliainen, Professor P. Johnsgard, Dr. I. Hjorth, Dr. R. Moss, Dr. H. J. Degn, Dr. P. Rajala, Dr. T. Lovel, Mr. K. Howman, Mr. E. Maclean, and many, many more.

Help has been offered in many ways including behavioural drawings from Dr. Scherzinger, references to their work by among others Professor Johnsgard and Dr. Hjorth, and photographs of excellent quality from people like Dr. Aschenbrenner.

Other access to photographic material was provided by VIREO in Philadelphia per Robert Cardillo, the other principal photographers include Eric Hosking OBE, Ken Fink, Hans Aschenbrenner, Tevvo Heitajärvi, David Lambie, John Bayliss, B. Veprintsev, H. Cruickshank, C. H. Greenwalt, Snr. Gutierrez, J. Dunning, D. Roby, Don MacCaskill, David Kent, and a few of my own.

The hopefully not too numerous errors and omissions are entirely mine. Of necessity certain species on the edge of the Region covered by this book have been omitted as the line had to be drawn at some point.

The gestation of this book has been rather more protracted than was originally planned as a result of events outside my control.

Vegetational Map of the Holarctic Region

Tundra
Boreal Forest
Alpine Vegetation
Temperate Forest
Prairie Grassland
Cold Steppe
Deciduous/Coniferous
Desert and Scrub
Mediterranean/Chaparral

Introduction

The purpose of this book is to take a detailed ornithological and avicultural look at those species of Gallinaceous birds whose natural distribution is to be found throughout the faunal area known as the Holeartic Region. This is more precisely defined by existing political boundaries as being: **North America from the Mexican border northwards, all of the European continent including the islands of the Mediterranean and all that part of Asia including and bounded to the south by Israel, Jordan, Iran, the Union of Soviet Socialist Republics, Central and Northern China, Korea, Mongolia and Japan.**

Gallinaceous birds are a very diverse group, ranging from species like the small but varied Quails, to the larger Pheasants, Grouse and Turkeys. Most of us living in this region have almost daily contact with another species which, although originating from within the region, is now found throughout the entire world. I am of course referring to the Jungle Fowls' domestic descendants, the ordinary Hen in its many varied shapes and sizes.

In the usual way, typical of Man, we are fairly poorly informed about these many species and their needs, and at the same time we are creating substantial problems for their continued survival by our pressure on their habitats. To some degree or other every species of living creature is restricted by the availability of its preferred habitat. In the case of Game Birds this is especially so, particularly for the forest species of Grouse and Pheasant.

With our seemingly insatiable demand for timber and forest products it is particularly important to understand the requirements of these species, and we must somehow make allowances for them. In this regard aviculturalists have already saved more than one species from extinction and will increasingly be more relied upon to hold population reservoirs while ornithologists and scientists establish the precise needs of any particular species, thereby making it possible for successful re-introductions to the wild at a later date.

Aviculturalists have proved a dedicated, if not masochistic, band of people upon whose future work ornithologists and scientists are likely to have to rely and which they will appreciate increasingly with the passage of time.

With increasing leisure time, greater availability of resources and better knowledge, larger numbers of individuals and organisations are now specialising in the undoubted challenges of breeding endangered and rare species in captivity. This is especially true of the Pheasant family, as the Galliformes are often described, and more and more governments in all parts of the world are recognising and encouraging this valuable contribution. In respect of over a third of the species considered in this text there is little or no record of their captive breeding, and this fact alone is challenge enough for most of us.

It is my hope that this book will prove of equal use to all interests and perhaps of some value to a few. There is nothing of much originality to be claimed for any of the contents. I regard it more as an edited collection of information, put together from many sources, including existing publications — some of which are variously generally available or more obscure — coupled to which I have added extra details obtained by correspondence with others without whose help and fullest co-operation this book would not have been possible.

Boat of Garten, Inverness-shire, Scotland   **Iain Brodie**

Chapter 1
Evolution of Gallinaceous Gamebirds

POSSIBLE ORIGINS

Evolution is perhaps the last aspect concerning Gallinaceous birds to be fully and accurately resolved, and in the foreseeable future this will probably remain so. While we remain lacking in facts, this will not prevent speculation and reasoned argument in the meantime. The consensus of opinion to date does, however, suggest that Proto-Galliformes originated from within a dense forest environment and I think one would go along with the view that this forest environment was most certainly tropical in nature on balance of probability.

Originally, the birds would probably have been terrestrial with a slightly later and parallel arboreal development. This would include the present day descendants of families and genera most of which are not covered within the geographical scope of this particular book. At some later stage, how much later remaining unknown as yet (and this may be so for the immediate future) there was was a northerly dispersal, colonizing the temperate forest, grassland and arid areas.

Professor Johnsgard in his book *Grouse and Quails of North America* is confidently assertive that Quail and Grouse originated in Central and Tropical America. This is somewhat bold, as we are considering a vast time scale when continental geography as we know it today was vastly different. For example, there is no doubt that Eastern North America was connected to Western Europe and South America to Africa, Antartica and Australia. Also, we must consider

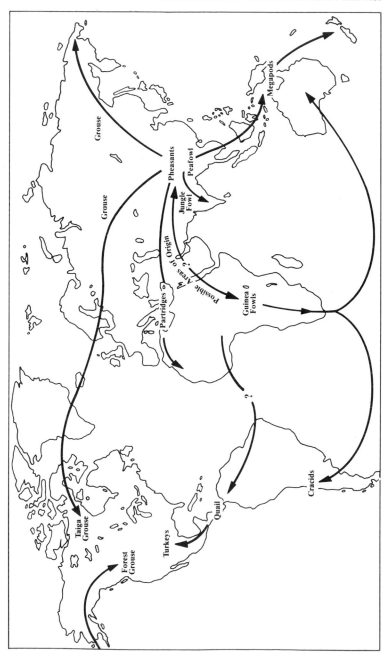

Figure 1.   Evolutionary Distribution Map

Asia where so many Pheasants, Quails, Grouse, and others are found. If we must make reference to existing continental geography then owing to the sheer diversity of genera, then it would not be surprising if Asia was the general centre for the ancestral Proto-Galliformes. Whatever the arguments no one has yet firm evidence and we must wait perhaps some time yet before we get it.

FAMILIES AND GENERA

Moving forward in time, we must consider the extant families and genera. Even with specimens available for study taxonomists are still in disagreement over degrees of relationship among species let alone among genera and families. The identifying by Holman of *Paleophasianus* from the Eocene period seems the earliest fossil evidence for modern Pheasants, if that is what it represents. The problem is where to go from there, and which developed from what and from where.

Although the Tropical regions are outside the scope of this book the origins of the birds dealt with here at some time had their beginnings probably in the Tropical Rain Forests but colonized the Temperate, Boreal and Tundra/Alpine habitats at a very early stage in their evolution.

The super family *Phasianidae* is commonly accepted as the principal taxonomical description for those species covered by this book, included in which are the sub-families of: *Meleagridinae* – Turkeys, *Odontophorinae* – New World Quails, *Phasianinae* – Old World Pheasants included in which are the Tribes; *Perdicini*, embracing Old World Partridges, Francolins and Quails; *Phasianini*, embracing Old World Pheasants, Jungle Fowl and Peafowl. The final sub-family is *Numidinae* – the Guinea Fowl of Africa which are, along with the Jungle Fowl and Peafowl, not considered here. Also outside the scope of this book is the Super family *Cracoidea* which incorporates the family *Megapodidae* from Asia, Polynesia and Australasia, and the family *Cracidae* from Central and South America. It is worth mentioning at this point that some authorities regard the Grouse as a full family as *Tetraonidae* and I am inclined to agree with this view, but the matter needs a full investigation.

One of the potential areas for future research lies within the exploration of genetic relationships through chromosome analysis and one certainly looks forward to seeing what such studies will produce, as they should take some of the guess-work out of everyone's theories and may clarify many relationships as yet only guessed at. If it is accepted that Gallinaceous birds originated from within a Tropical Forest habitat it is also highly probable that latitudinal and altitudinal diversities originated a very long time ago and it will be most unlikely that precise family and genera relationships can be linked up now, so we must consider each independently of the others and devote attention to relationships between genera and among species.

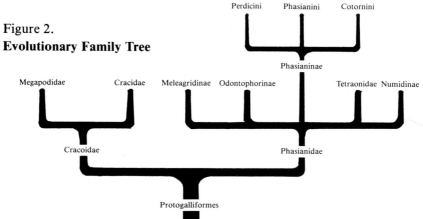

Figure 2.
Evolutionary Family Tree

Note:
The time scale is not known from Proto-Galliformes but must exceed 50 million years and may well be closer to 100 million years.

Evolutionary relationships and developments are dictated by habitat availability and appropriate adaptation to changing or prevailing conditions. The birds considered in this book show how full advantage can be taken from by this radiating out of one forest type into another, from forest to steppe, arid desert, montane and tundra habitats. This dispersal, apart from being latitudinal and altitudinal in aspect, was in some instances also longitudinal and all of these movements would be conditional on climatic variations, by both the advance and recession of glaciation, and/or the increase or decrease in precipitation. The final and not insignificant factor is further speciation, or extermination, with Man having a notable localizing effect on the latter with potential to cause total extermination on a short time scale. In the case of Speciation, Man has already moved at least one species, the true Pheasant, some way down the road in a comparatively short time towards producing several sub-species.

In considering the Quails, the Old World-Palearctic species, *Cotornix*, has a remarkable distribution range with only minimal plumage variations, yet over a smaller geographical area the New World-Nearctic species are diverse to a remarkable degree both generically and specifically. We are fortunate in that Professor Johnsgard has made a very careful and exhaustive study of these birds and, by means of a series of breeding experiments has produced a range of hybrids which, when set out in his subsequent table, illustrates certain aspects of relationships very well indeed. He went on to elaborate further by recording details of resulting fertility in a fascinating way.

HYBRIDS

Hybridization *per se* for "amusement", by accident or through idle curiosity is to be frowned upon, but if Johnsgard's principles were to be followed in respect of the Pheasants, Grouse, Partridges and Francolins (especially the Pheasants and Grouse), a lot of interesting information might result which could give some indications as to relative relationships and possible lines of descent. Some of these hybrids have already been produced but as they were usually accidental, apart from noting their occurrence, few have been described in detail and almost no attempts have been made to check for fertility, reciprocosity, back-crossing, voice and behaviour. Obviously, such work would be immensely time consuming and expensive; furthermore, in the absence of commercial objectives or returns, it seems unlikely to be undertaken by other than the most dedicated and well-heeled avicultural enthusiast. In relative terms the Pheasants would be easiest to work with due to the greater ease with which these birds can be kept in captivity.

Other avenues in which relationships can be explored include territorial display and advertisement, and reproductive display, which Ingemar Hjorth has done really well amongst the Grouse. Similarities in reproductive display will prove a much safer indication of evolutionary relationships than will apparent physical similarities as the latter may well have developed from habitat selection pressures, although it need not be discounted entirely at the outset. Vocal similarities may also be helpful, using sonograms, and a fair amount of work in this direction has already been done with certain Pheasants and Grouse in North America, Japan and Sweden, as well as Scotland.

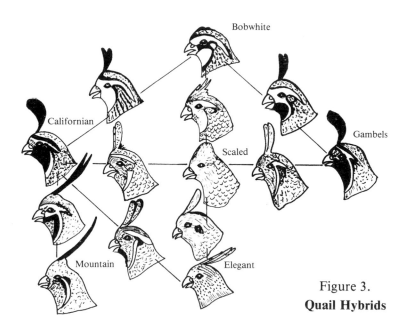

Bobwhite

Californian

Gambels

Scaled

Mountain

Elegant

Figure 3.
Quail Hybrids

DIAGRAMS AND CHARTS

The accompanying diagrams and charts attempt to show possible evolutionary directions which are little better than wild guesses and conjecture. It simply is not possible with our present state of knowledge to do anything other than guess especially when paleontologists cannot agree on Man's ancestry, advent or geographical origins — almost every year evidence is uncovered pushing the time scale further and further back. As an example, perfect footprints of 17 species of birds and animals dating from 3.5 million years ago have been exposed and identified around Lake Eyasi, Tanzania, in volcanic ash. These footprints show quite positively Francolins and Guinea Fowl no different from those that might be obtained today, so we are forced into reasoned guesswork.

Within each habitat type there are a number of ecological niches that are open to exploitation by varying degrees by all forms of living organisms and, in order to successfully exploit a selected resource, a particular size or form of behaviour may be necessary, which accounts for the considerable diversity of families of game birds. In the Paleoarctic region of the Old World, Gallinaceous birds have evolved species of Grouse, Quail, Pheasant, Snow Cock, Partridge and Francolin, while in the Nearctic region of the New World we only find Grouse, Turkey and Quail. When the corresponding Southern Hemisphere regions are considered we have on the one hand Fowls such as Peafowls, Guinea Fowls and Megapods while on the other hand we only have in the Neotropical area Chachalacas, Curassows and Guans. With only one third of the species to be found in the New World and two thirds in the Old World we can look to the latter as the most likely place of origin for our ancestral Galliforme birds.

While everyone is agreed on the existence at some stage of a common ancestry amongst this group, I suspect few appreciate that the time scale is incredibly long; in fact it is positively vast and a figure of at least 10 million years for some genera would not surprise many experts. It should also be borne in mind that just because Quails as one group, for example, are superficially similar in size, it does not follow necessarily that New and Old World Quails are closely related — quite the reverse. They may in fact not be very close at all, having evolved simultaneously from an already divergent ancestor to take advantage of habitat availability in what then were, perhaps, entirely different geographical areas from those they now find themselves in.

It is not the authors intention to consider the possible Primitive-Gallinaceous relationships, as I certainly feel neither competent nor confident enough to do so. What might, however, be worth consideration is the evolution of species and genera and the reasons for their development occurring as it did.

Pheasants of the Temperate Zone seem at an early stage in their development to have secured a virtually impregnable hold throughout this type of habitat. These birds moved out to evolve either altitudinally or latitudinally and take advantage of adjacent areas such as forest margins, and then further upward into montane habitats. There are also the adjacent steppe or arid habitats as well as the moorland and tundra, all of which have been taken advantage of by one or more species, either exclusively or at varying stages in that habitat's vegetational successions, as is most obvious in the differing age classes in a forest's succession.

Considering the Pheasants, those from the areas of densest forest undergrowth are most clearly and brilliantly coloured, always in the cocks that is, for example, in the Golden Pheasant, the hens need their cryptical dark colouration as a means of survival. Progressing into forest with less dense undergrowth either by travelling further North, or altitudinally. Species such as the Reeves and Elliots Pheasants may be noticeably attractive, but they are not so extreme. Eventually, we come to the so called "true" Pheasants which, while still remaining dimorphic, are very much subdued in colouration on account of their very open type of habitat and the greater security their plumage gives them. An example of how this works in practice: after an extreme gale which affected my own avaries all my Pheasants escaped when the netting over their aviaries was ripped away. I was able to find, in respect of the Golden and Amherst species, the remains of all the cock birds within 24 hours, taken by Peregrine Falcons and Common Buzzards. The hens lasted much longer and both sexes of True Pheasants after a year and more still feed around the house and sometimes even with the domestic poultry, only now they bring their offspring too! One can only presume that on account of size the Eared Pheasants have less to fear from avian predators and do not find their colouration a significant handicap — both sexes are similar.

The Grouse is undoubtedly the most successful temperate region group, found as they are with both an Old World and New World distribution. Some species are even circumpolar in their distribution, doubtless due to the virtually contiguous geographical areas of suitable habitat they occupy. The Lagopus genus has only evolved limited speciation to the south of their ranges in two cases, one in North America, which is the Whitetailed Ptarmigan, and the other in Europe, the Red Grouse. Both are due to their geographical isolation.

Clearly, the matter of the other Grouse species and their true relationships is currently the subject of much debate and likely to continue to be so for some time. While in terms of size the New

World Turkey comes nearest to that of the Capercaillie, it seems likely that the New World Blue Grouse and Spruce Grouse show more than a passing likeness in many particulars to the Capercaillie and all three share similar habitats in addition to the presence of one species, the Siberian Spruce Grouse, in the Old World, which is rather suggestive of possible relationships.

Blue Eared Pheasant

Sage Grouse

Chapter 2
Conservation of Gamebirds

Before proceeding too far, it should be said that the term 'Game Birds' in this context is restricted to those *Galliformes* birds covered by this book. It is, however, appreciated that the term is sometimes used to include other groups such as Waders and Waterfowl. It is an undeniable facet of Man's nature and behaviour that those things which he greatly desires are the things which he greatly protects. In a wildlife context this means legal restrictions by Man's societies to make available certain things at a price under a constructed set of rules, often for the benefit of a self perceived elite in former times. To a lesser extent, this is true today. Custom has bent before the winds of change and adapted by making itself available to more people and thereby surviving.

It is a tragic aspect to this situation that those species not held in high esteem – for whatever reason – are those which are at greatest risk from Man's activities. In one example we have the extermination of the Capercaillie in Scotland during the late 18th century almost exclusively because of habitat disruption and destruction. By the late 19th century, however, what do we find but the Capercaillie back in Scotland, and expanding rapidly due to habitat reconstruction by re-afforestation in the first instance; but equally important was the notion to shoot numbers for sport. Presumably, as with a new toy, everyone aspired to bag this strange and great Grouse as a trophy. To this end every effort was made to propagate and spread the species again. Its relationship to its habitat was only slightly appreciated.

After the initial euphoria died down most people forgot the Caper-caillie in Scotland. Its continued survival was barely noticed, nor was its expansion apart from the curiosity value of the odd bird bagged for a trophy. Numbers became so high in some areas that the bird was thought of, and treated as, a forest pest and controlled on that basis. In the last decade or two Continental European shooters have expressed interest and offered to pay for the chance to shoot this species. Suddenly in Scotland the Capercaillie has changed from a pest to an asset and is managed, which implies an element of preser-vation to achieve the best return for the landowner in these egali-tarian times, not through shooting by himself but by his shooting tenants.

While we sustain the Capercaillie in Scotland by shooting driven birds, which is a form of natural selection, we have the sad experience of decline rather rapidly of this species in Central Europe, due to a totally different and very unnatural selection through stalking the master cocks at the spring lek. By the very simple means of removing the best genetic material consistently the vitality of these populations is, or has, collapsed as it logically must. Yet I have sat and listened to very intelligent and articulate men argue that almost every other fact was responsible, then seek advice on how best to continue the art of the impossible.

Personally, I hold no brief for the anti-shooting league, but I do believe that it is an essential tool of conservation to know what a natural population can sustain as a harvestable proportion, and fail to see any merit in manipulating a population and its habitat to arti-ficially increase the yield of birds that may be shot by 'desk cowboys' of old, and young men with protruding stomachs. Such manipulation incurs a cost factor which might seem to be just cash, but is almost invariably at the expense of the habitat and other components of that habitat, e.g. avian and mammalian predators, all of which constitute part of these habitats.

Broadening the subject of habitat for this wonderful family of birds, we can identify certain habitat types: tundra, moorland and montane in which are situated the Ptarmigan type Grouse and Monals. This is followed by those species inhabiting broken forest and forest margins where the Eared Pheasants, Black Grouse and others are found in a basically boreal environment. The next group are the Forest exclusive species such as the Elliot's and Golden Pheasants, Spruce Grouse and Capercaillie. Finally, there are the

Lowland cultivation and steppe type species including the Quails, Partridges and True Pheasants. By considering carefully each habitat type it will be possible to gain some measure of vulnerability for any given species and if necessary a 'vulnerability factor' can be calculated, taking habitat into account with other considerations.

TUNDRA, MOORLAND MONTANE

Perhaps the least vulnerable of all habitats, due to inaccessibility, is that which is also most hostile. The inaccessibility is either altitudinally or latitudinally, or both. Not everyone wants to climb mountains or holiday in the Arctic, but Man does achieve an impact on these regions, albeit at second hand, through pollution in the form of acid precipitation blown north. This has a direct effect through the food chain on the insects so vital to chicks in their first few weeks of life not just by the simple protein value but also quantity and quality being affected. Apart from this rather insidious aspect, one can safely say that this must constitute the most secure of habitats being considered.

FOREST MARGINS, OPEN FOREST

While this may be a definable type, its nature and content vary in shape and density, and from this its carrying capacity for associated wildlife species must also vary. Averaged out, however, there can be a reasonably constant capacity which allows for a population surplus. The usual threat to this type of habitat is from overgrazing by domestic livestock as a rule, and by deer over-population due to lack of hunting pressure from major predators – either greatly reduced now or exterminated altogether in many areas. Fire can have a catastrophic short-term effect and there is, lastly, felling of trees for firewood. Perhaps this last factor is only of local significance in under-developed areas.

TRUE FOREST

This must be without a doubt the most significant type of habitat. Its importance cannot be overrated, and yet this is the most threatened of all. The threats are several: over-exploitation, outright clearance, replacement with a monoculture of single species having a theoretically higher timber yield in an obsessively short time scale. It does not require much imagination to understand the significance of total clearance of forest on forest-dependent species, but there are more subtle significances which in some cases are not yet fully understood in respect of over-exploitation of any renewable resource, from whatever standpoint. In respect of the Pheasant family, after canopy cover is reduced beyond the minimum, populations just collapse. This happens also when the shrub layer of a forest is destroyed or removed, often due to domestic livestock browsing plant species which are very important to these and other forest dependent species. This type of damage is certainly not confined to the under-developed countries. Right here on my own doorstep in Scotland, despite laws which have existed for nearly 400 years prohibiting grazing of domestic livestock in forests, the practice is very prevalent. This leads to a massive decline in our native forests, this being particularly accelerated with changing land use over the last 100−200 years as a result of the large scale ranching of sheep in the northern and southern mountains in this country.

Modern forestry practice leads to a tendency to pursue reafforestation using single species which no formal forest is, or ever has been, composed of, and to have large areas of the same age class − again a most unnatural situation, causing tremendous disruption when the crop is harvested over such a large area at any one time. Choice of tree species can prove equally disastrous when re-planting and again the worst offender I know of in Europe is the Forestry Commission in Scotland who use 80% of the non-native Sitka Spruce *(picea sitchensis)*.

Fire within a forest is of only short-term disadvantage, because it very quickly develops a shrub layer largely of food species which is followed by re-afforestation, providing the area is not grazed by domestic livestock or overstocked with deer. Forest clearance on a large scale is nowadays unusual in most parts of the geographical area covered by this book, with the exception of some parts of China. This, as we all know, is not the case in the Tropical regions to the South of the Holarctic.

CULTIVATED LOWLANDS

Formerly most of this habitat would have been forest of one sort or another. Nowadays it constitutes a significant and valuable habitat

Figure 4. **Habitat Zones**

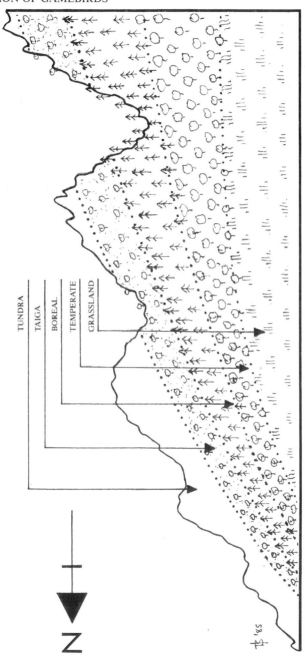

for all the Quails, Partridges and the True Pheasants. Because these regions are densely inhabited by Man, there is in some senses high pressure on these birds' populations through disturbance, shooting and pesticides. Nevertheless, the same shooting interests are responsible for substantial numbers of birds being aritifically reared every year. These numbers must amount to several million annually, worldwide.

As long as there are people who want to shoot these birds they will remain secure, as great effort and expense are devoted to catching up breeding stock in the winter, breeding and rearing. Special arrangements for extra feeding, and land set aside for shelter, ensure higher numbers than would naturally be supported by a wild population, even under the most favourable conditions.

CONCLUSIONS

With very few exceptions none of the Pheasant family represented in the Holarctic Region are actually endangered in the wild. A number are, however, threatened, which must make us aware of the possibility of further decline. This is all the more so with species whose distribution and requirements for future survival are not well known or not known at all.

Slowly but surely research is being started for many species, in order to know and to understand their individual requirements. This is the beginning; it is an essential start being done for us all by scientists and highly motivated amateurs. The shooting lobby have developed the basics for rearing various species and it is from this rather long established expertise.

The future for securing the long-term existence of the bird species considered here is to establish for each species in detail their individual habitat requirements, their natural and avicultural propagation with a view to maintenance and, wherever necessary, re-establishment and a full consideration of a species' limitations including diet, behaviour, reproduction, tolerance levels for physical and environmental disturbance through pollution and Man's recreational and other activities. It should be possible to establish a 'vulnerability factor' based on detailed knowledge of a species. This can be used to identify the overall status of a species throughout its distribution and also its local status, which would be most helpful to anticipate and arrest any declines before they become unmanageable in these areas.

Perhaps a scale of one to five can be used overall, with the same scale used for individual factors which can then be summarised producing a mean figure on the overall vulnerability. The advantage of applying the 'vulnerability factor' to individual species enables problems to be identified easily and remedies can be sought and applied, thus reducing the mean.

With a scale of one to five a suggested classification could be as follows:—

1. Numerous
2. Common
3. Uncommon
4. Rare
5. Endangered

To arrive at this vulnerability factor a total will be achieved by summarising several composites, the parts of which could be made up in the following way:—

1. Habitat Destruction
2. Hunting Pressure
3. Recreational Pressure
4. Predation
5. Disease

Figure 5.   **Vulnerability Factor**

Example:—

CAPERCAILLIE IN SCOTLAND	
1. HABITAT DESTRUCTION	3
2. HUNTING PRESSURE	2
3. RECREATIONAL PRESSURE	1
4. NATURAL PREDATION	2
5. DISEASE and PARASITES	3
5 $\sqrt{}$ 11	
VULNERABILITY Uncommon +	2.2

Assessing the composites is so very much subject to individual assessments and perceptions that this could be where the assessment has potential for failure or criticism. Obviously the sooner each species can be studied and assessed the better. A start is being made, and through the forum of organisations like the World Pheasant Association ideas and information are being exchanged, promoted and, most importantly, implemented! We can only expect to know what we should be doing when we know in full what each species needs, and ought to be able to expect from Man, to satisfy its own particular needs and therefore sustain its future for all time. This is the least we can do.

Chapter 2.1

Conservation and Aviculture

The importance of the role of aviculture in conservation cannot be over-stated, nor should it be under-valued, forming as it does the ultimate defence for an endangered species when it faces extermination. I cannot conceive of any circumstance within our present knowledge and experience when any species of mammal or bird need ever again be lost through extinction and extermination. There are, however, a not insignificant number of people who do feel that if a species cannot sustain itself in the wild it should be just allowed to go. Such a view, in my estimation, serves to illustrate the breadth of ignorance the holder has of mankind's disproportionate ability to destroy and disrupt all aspects of the environment in which he finds himself and all those components which go into making that environment tolerable and ultimately viable. If we were all to adopt such a negative attitude and abdicate our responsibility so easily as far as birds are concerned for example, then where is it all to stop? Do we keep this insect, that plant, these fish? Logically we would all end up sitting watching the desert sands trickling through our fingers, but of course we would not last that long if for no other reason than that every living thing is but a small part of the whole and every link lost makes the chain that much weaker, with compound interest! The biggest question, of course, is not who will decide but have we the right to decide? Quite obviously we do not have that right although some of us may wish to assume it and while it may be easy to say 'let it go' it is a lot harder by far to say 'save it' because that requires effort and a commitment both in time and resources.

This commitment makes aviculturists a special type of person, singularly strong willed, inquisitive and, dare I say, resourceful. Also amongst this group of people there are a small number who are gifted; they have the initiative, foresight and imagination to lead the way. In the Gamebird world the doyen must of course be Dr. Jean Delacour and his collection at Cleres, France. Many of the initiatives in work among the Pheasants follow on from his early efforts and ideas. He could never have imagined the far-reaching implications of his searches and collecting in what was then known as French Indo-China. Where, for example, would the Imperial Pheasant be? – probably just a brief description and a painting in a book some 30 years old. Well, the Imperial Pheasant is now reprieved, more or less intact, with Amsterdam Zoo picking up the torch and London Zoo providing a back-up reserve. Further species probably saved by captive propagation include Humes Pheasant, Mikado Pheasant and Elliots, all of which have, along with the Imperial Pheasant, been the subject of the most massive habitat assault ever seen during the various Indo-Chinese conflicts which are probably not yet over.

More recently and most successfully the Cheer Pheasant has been, and is being, actively returned from the brink of extinction in a spectacular way through the activities of British aviculturists working through the World Pheasant Association who are co-ordinating the programme with the Pakistan Government. It is undoubtedly in this direction that future conservation must be directed, the aviculturists holding, propagating and securing a species, while those in other fields can resolve habitat difficulties, control and protection in order that restocking of these habitats can be successfully accomplished with the captively produced birds. Currently Capercaillie are being re-introduced to Italy; it may be possible also to restock Black Grouse in Holland and Denmark, and Capercaillie in England, Ireland and Germany. Other species such as the Sage Grouse, Pinnated Grouse and Common Partridge could also be propagated and re-introduced into former parts of their range from which they are now absent due to changed land use, over-hunting and reduced food resources as a result of excessive insecticide usage.

There is an increasing recognition, particularly amongst West European governments, of the value of aviculture as a tool in conservation, but without any actual involvement and encouragement. Perhaps in a perverse way this is all to the good with regard to the individualistic nature of most aviculturists. Providing aviculturists can come across with the goods when required and make it common knowledge to the general public just who is producing the necessary birds, and how they are doing it, then there must be an assured future and most probably an increasing demand for their expertise.

In terms of promoting the constructive aspects of Aviculture perhaps the most successful, albeit young, organisation, is the World Pheasant Association, based in the United Kingdom where it was founded by extremely progressive aviculturists, now with many national Chapters worldwide. The World Pheasant Association is very worthwhile for all sorts of reasons, not the least of which is members' ability to freely exchange information on all aspects and problems, thereby quickly bringing a wide section of aviculturists right up to date very quickly. The World Pheasant Association rightly adopts a high profile, actively promoting its activities, aims and objectives. As in the case of the work with the Cheer Pheasant, these are now producing results of a very tangible nature which are there for all to see.

While numerous species of gamebirds are not in any way endangered they need not be regarded as of any less importance or significance. It is these species which act as a good and sound training ground for progressing to more difficult and endangered ones. It is far better to gain experience and, if need be, make one's mistakes working with those birds whose numbers and future are not likely to be affected by such losses which cannot be avoided by all of us when starting up with whatever group of birds we are interested in.

In fulfilling a role in conservation it is important, in fact vital, that the aviculturist is aware of some very important points concerning those birds which find themselves in his care. It is undoubtedly true that many, if not most, aviculturists keeping any of the Gamebirds are attracted very often by the beauty of the bird's plumage and behaviour in the first instance, having little concern for any involvement in propagating a rare species 'per se'. There are really two major factors which must be kept to the fore; firstly there is the need to minimise or avoid altogether any risk of inbreeding; secondly, and not nearly so easily monitored, is the very considerable and real danger of 'domestication', as the colour mutants of the Golden Pheasant show.

Inbreeding is not nearly well enough understood – the majority of aviculturists are still selling almost all of their surplus birds as pairs, and clearly a like number of people purchase them in this way, which is totally wrong. This sooner rather than later must lead to inbreeding, bringing with it all sorts of genetically associated problems and defects including loss of fertility and libido, which has already occurred with some of the Pheasants. Leg and foot defects may also occur, as too could eyesight difficulties and so forth. Domestication, as previously mentioned, is not easily monitored, and it is not at all easy to define either. If we consider the Hawaiian Goose, or Ne-ne, as a case in point it will be seen what can happen in a short time.

The Hawaiian Goose population was reduced to a very low number, which obviously restricted the gene-pool, putting the population further at risk. A very laudable decision was made to attempt to rescue the species with a significant proportion of the population being removed for captive breeding. These birds were further split up into smaller groups in which successful breeding took place repeatedly until all birds in each group were closely related and as subsequent generations were dispersed they too bred amongst themselves. This was bad enough, but one further factor which had not been taken into account was the simple fact that these Geese frequently walk around on the very uneven surface of the steep lava flows, a terrain which encouraged the development of long and strong legs in order to negotiate this type of habitat. In captivity, after just a few short decades, it was noticed that these birds' legs were slowly but surely shortening in length as they adapted to their new environment. Fortunately this trend was identified before it had gone too far and in time for a number of birds to be returned to be released in Hawaii. One further problem was a physical deformity resulting from this inbreeding and those birds had to be vigorously culled out of the captive population. The Ne-ne has fortunately been saved, but aviculturists have, or should have, learned a lot from this situation; it can happen again to any species of mammal or bird, especially with those whose numbers have fallen to a very low level.

One example of the positive measures which can be taken is to be seen with the register of the population of the Cheer Pheasant maintained by the World Pheasant Association, which enables aviculturists keeping this species to locate unrelated specimens for pairing up. By continually out-crossing in such a manner there does seem little likelihood of any hereditary defects manifesting themselves amongst the captive population. Natural selection pressures dictate that rarely more than 50% of juveniles will survive long enough to reproduce; the remainder will have succumbed to predation by either birds or animals, some to disease and some just are not genetically strong enough to survive.

In aviculture we all strive to rear the greatest number we can from those we hatch, yet is this 'success' rate necessarily altogether a wise yardstick? Could it not be that some of these young birds are pre-determined not to survive? This certainly seems to be so. By the same token the fact that whenever possible we use all our progeny to breed from must imply that we are building into future generations an obviously inherent risk. It is for this reason that I am not too worried by losing a few birds, but if this proportion ever exceeded 30% I would be rather concerned.

It is incumbent on aviculturists working with a species which has one or more sub-species that these be kept pure and not mixed in any way. Natural selection has evolved these races for specific reasons and they are what they are because of these selection pressures. Hybridisation between true species for other than serious scientific study is clearly quite wrong; it undoubtedly does happen either through idle curiosity or carelessness, but whatever the excuse it shows a fine disregard for the welfare of both parental species as the young birds are back-crossed into one or both parents' stock, thereby adulterating them too. Alternatively, they just amount to a rather sad curiosity, not wanted by anyone and totally useless, repre-senting as they do a waste of resources and material.

The importance of maintaining pure stocks of such sub-species as exist is essential when a project for re-introduction is considered. By international agreement any re-introduction of a species to its former habitat must use birds or animals from the nearest available population geographically to that which is being replaced. This has been adopted for sound reasons to ensure the suitability of the re-introduced specimens to the habitat in which they must again establish themselves. Aviculturists directly involved in the task of producing birds for re-introduction to the wild either to re-populate an area or reinforce a depleted population face some singularly diffi-cult problems, all of which are associated with survival after release.

In the case of all forms of birds one common problem is that of food foraging. The other major problem peculiar to some forms is that of predation and each will be dealt with in turn. Successful foraging in the case of gamebirds has to be carefully considered and the problem approached well in advance of any contemplated release of these birds. While much of their time is given over to foraging, this activity must always be considered in the light of the birds needing to maintain a substantial degree of wariness.

Prior to release feeding should be supplemented as far as possible with a wide range of natural foods which are currently available, thereby reducing the time inexperienced birds have to spend experimenting with unfamiliar sources in an unfamiliar situation. The time they can devote to actually eating rather than searching greatly enhances their survival, allowing for greater fitness and vigilance. Collection and freezer storage is a useful precaution. Ideally the release pen should be located in a secure position right in the area

Figure 6.   **Light and Seclusion Pen**

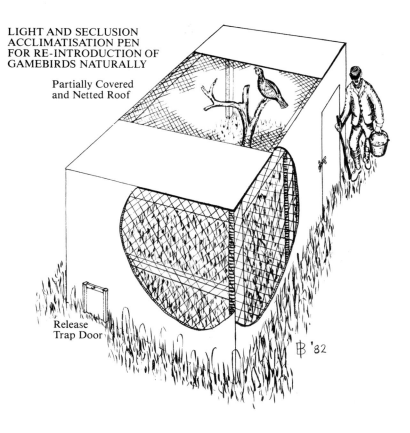

LIGHT AND SECLUSION
ACCLIMATISATION PEN
FOR RE-INTRODUCTION OF
GAMEBIRDS NATURALLY

Partially Covered
and Netted Roof

Release
Trap Door

$\mathbb{B}$ '82

the birds will actually be expected to survive in. This has a number of advantages including a very important familiarisation with their surroundings, the local light conditions and the other occupants of that habitat. To a large extent this will limit the chances of a rapid dispersal with the attendant problems of disorientation and reduced contact amongst the birds which is so vital to avoid at this stage. A further advantage in adopting this release method is the ease with which various locally abundant and utilisable foods can be brought in regularly to assist in the familiarisation process which will prove so beneficial at a later date. After release it also gives a locus for the birds to return to, enabling them to be given slowly declining quantities of supplementary feeding which can be scattered over an increasingly wide area, also reducing the risk of predators becoming familiar with the inexperienced birds' behaviour.

Any people regularly involved in feeding these birds at all stages in their development should announce their arrival and presence by a repetitive call, words or whistle to which the birds, both pre-release and post-release can associate with food availability. This approach to feeding is also effective in another way, in that it avoids panic amongst the birds without making them over-familiar with humans who could be other than favourably disposed to them either at that time or when they are mature.

The second and rather more drastic problem of conditioning birds pre-release is that of avoiding predation. This is what is known as developing an adequate 'flight response' without which the predation rate would be almost certainly either total or so nearly so as to make little difference. The result would be failure. In order to avoid this position arising the rearing procedure for birds to be released can be modified sufficiently easily to allow the birds to develop their natural 'flight responses' fully and effectively, ensuring the birds are fully wild in as near as natural a state as is possible for birds reared under artificial conditions. A system of rearing in pens best described as 'light and seclusion' is fairly effective. Clearly it is not possible to avoid the young birds seeing the human form entirely, but it is important to restrict access to as few people as possible, perhaps one or two, and for them to make themselves familiar in the manner described above. Under no circumstances should dogs or other domestic animals be visible to the penned birds; this has the effect of ensuring a suitable 'flight response' when the birds later see foxes, badgers and other mammalian predators. Provision of suitable ground cover such as brushwood, tree branches, etc., makes ideal areas for the birds to retreat into and hide from avian predators which are quite likely to fly over and perch on the pens and their roof netting. This point is rather important, especially so for the hens which must develop as fully as possible the ability to 'freeze' which will greatly minimise the chances of their being located while brooding their nests the following year.

In conclusion there is one final method of re-introducing Gamebirds where an appropriate species can be found, and this is known as 'Cross Fostering'. This was first used successfully in Scotland when the first ever re-introduction of any species to its former habitat was attempted. Capercaillie eggs were brought from Scandinavia and put under Black Grouse hens; this did prove most effective and led to a rapid re-colonisation in subsequent years. It is my belief that this method might well be successfully tried if any attempts are contemplated for other species, e.g. Black Grouse under Caucasian Pheasants, Capercaillie again under Black Grouse, and several of the Asiatic Pheasants under one another.

Chapter 2.2

International Controls and Licensing of Endangered Species

With the increased awareness amongst several Western governments that the continuing exploitation of wildlife resources through over hunting, trapping and collecting, all the more evident after the Second World War, it became more and more important that some system or systems of control, balances and checks be implemented particularly by the 'consumer' countries. The philosophy in part quite rightly seems to have been that by limiting numbers and availability greater efforts might be devoted to the care and welfare of specimens already in captivity, encouragement of their captive propagation which in most cases was never contemplated, considered, nor, as often happens, even attempted. Such breeding as may have occurred was invariably accidental and not infrequently resulted in inter-specific hybrids.

The change in the situation from one where the cost of breeding accommodation was vastly greater than the cost of replacement livestock to one where the revenue from captive reproduction became a significant part of the overall calculation, though enhanced value caused by declining availability, has led to a radical change, almost revolutionary in fact, and one which at the end of the 1970's bore almost no relationship to that which existed at the start of the 1970's.

The principal international agreement that started off the change is known as the Washington Convention in short, or more properly

The Convention on International Trade in Endangered Species of Wild Fauna and Flora, March 1973 (abbreviated as C.I.T.E.S.). It is open for all sovereign governments to adopt the Convention and ratify it by becoming signatories. Subsequently the European Parliament adopted the Convention in November 1981. Interestingly, it is not just the developed countries who are the only signatories; many non-developed or Third World countries are also now involved, which is equally important as they are the main source of origin for many of the gamebird and other species, particularly the Pheasants. It is no coincidence that management, housing and breeding techniques have significantly improved, as has the range and depth of knowledge, directly as a result of the establishment of the Washington Convention, which can only be a good thing ultimately resulting not just in contributing to the conservation of a species in its native environment but also in the long-term ensuring the continued availability of livestock for aviculturists of all kinds and scientists to work with. The Convention does not seek to ban trade in any species; it only seeks to control, manage and promote valid, acceptable uses while avoiding the risks of the previously obvious plundering of all wildlife.

The Washington Convention identifies two groups or categories of species:–

List A which are endangered species and subject to rigorous controls including intended use. This list is restrictive and licences are limited.

List B consists of species which are monitored and controlled species; List A which are endangered species and subject to rigorous controls including intended use. This list is restrictive and licences are limited. List B consists of species which are monitored and controlled for which licences must be applied (these are usually granted). Species listed in either group may be changed from one to the other as their changed status might warrant. Sadly those changes which occur are usually movements of a species or even an entire family to List A from List B. By implication there is a third list comprising species not controlled and not referred to in List A or B by reason of their substantial numbers and relative security. For those aviculturists and others dealing with any country which is a member of the European Community there is a modification of the Convention lists, namely the listing of species under List A as Endangered and 'Excepted Kinds'. Nothing is simple and if the EEC can make it difficult, it will do this, as there are numerous species neither identified in List A or as 'Excepted Kinds'.

The following is a record of those species under List A and 'Excepted'.

List A	White Eared Pheasant	*Crossoptilon crossoptilon*
	Brown Eared Pheasant	*Crossoptilon mantchuricum*
	Himalayan Monal	*Lophophurus impejanus*
	Chinese Monal	*Lophophurus lhuysii*
	Sclater's Monal	*Lophophurus sclater*
	Elliot's Pheasant	*Syrmaticus ellioti*
	Mikado Pheasant	*Syrmaticus mikado*
	Caspian Snowcock	*Tetraogallus caspus*
	Tibetan Snowcock	*Tetraogallus tibetanus*

Excepted Kinds

	Caucasian Pheasant	*Phasianus colchicus*
	Green Pheasant	*Phasianus versicolor*

The above species are those covered by the geographical area referred to in this book. Other listed species outside this area are not included here.

The following is a list of those countries which are signatories to the Washington Convention and are covered by the geographical areas referred to, along with the addresses of the relevant licence issuing authorities in these countries:—

Australia	No information.
Canada	The Administrator, C.I.T.E.S., Canadian Wildlife Service, Department of the Environment, Ottowa, Ontario K1A 0E7.
China	Endangered Species Import and Export Office, Ministry of Forestry, Hepingli BEIJING (PEKING).
Cyprus	Ministry of Agriculture and Natural Resources, Nicosia.

Denmark	Fredningsstyrelsen Miljøministeriet, Amaliegade 13, DK–1256 KOBENHAVN K.
Finland	Maa-ja Metsatalousministerio, Ministry of Agriculture and Forestry, Bureau of Natural Resources, Vuorikatu 16. SF–00100, HELSINKI 10.
France	Direction de la Protection de la Nature, Convention de Washington, Ministere de l'Environnement, 14 Bld. du General Lecler, F–92522 NEUILLY-SUR-SEINE.
German Democratic Republic	Ministerium für Land, Först und Nahrungsguterwirtschaft, Kepenicker Allee 39-57, DDR–1157 BERLIN.
German Federal Republic	Bundesministerium für Ernagrung, Landwirtschaft und Försten, Referat 623, Postfach 140270, D–5300 BONN 1.
Iran	Department of the Environment, P.O. Box 1430, TEHRAN.
Israel	Nature Reserves Authority, 78 Yirmeyahu Street, Hirmeyahu, JERUSALEM 94467.
Italy	Ministerio dell Agricoltura and dell Foreste, Divisione 11 Via G Carducci 5, 1–00187 ROMA.
Japan	Ministry of International Trade and Industry, International Affairs Division, 3-1 Kasumigaseki 1–chome, Chiyoda–ku. TOKYO.

Jordan	Royal Society for the Conservation of Nature, P.O. Box 6354, AMMAN.
Liechtenstein	See Switzerland.
Norway	Miljoverndepartmentet, Ministry of Environment, Postboks 8013 Dep, N–OSLO 1.
Sweden	Lantbruksstyrelsen, Vallgatan 8, S–551 83 JONJOPING.
Switzerland	Office Veterinaire Federal, Thunstrasse 17, CH–3005 BERNE 6.
United Kingdom (Scotland & England)	Department of the Environment, Tollgate House, Houlton Street, BRISTOL BS2 9DJ.
United States of America	Chief of Federal Wildlife, Permit Office, Fish and Wildlife Service, Department of the Interior, WASHINGTON DC 20240.
Union of Soviet Socialist Republics	Main Administration for Nature Conservation, Nature Reserves, Forestry and Game, Glavpriroda, Ministry of Agriculture of the USSR, Orlikov per 1/11, MOSCOW 107139.

In addition to the above States the following are a list of countries who are not signatories but who have controlling agencies for wildlife.

Albania	No information.

Belgium	Administration des eaux et forets, Ministere de la region wallone, 13 chaussee d'Ixelles, B–1050 BRUXELLES.
Bulgaria	Vice-ministere des forets et de la protection de l'environnement, 17 Rue Autime I, SOFIA.

Czechoslovakia	State Institute for the
	    Protection of Monuments and
	    Conservation of Nature,
	Valdstejnske Nam. 1,
	11801–PRAHA 1.

Greece	Ministry of Agriculture, Directorate General of Forests, 3-5 Ippokratous Street, ATHENS 135.
Hungary	National Office of Nature Conservation, BUDAPEST Pf 33.
Iceland	Ministry of Culture and Education, Hverfisgata 6, REYKJAVIK.
Iraq	State Organisation for Exports, P.O. Box 5670, Saadoum Street, BAGHDAD.
Ireland	Forest and Wildlife Service, Department of Lands, 22 Upper Merrion Street, DUBLIN 2.
Lebanon	No information.
Malta	Ministry of Agriculture and Fisheries, 3A Old Mint Street, VALLETTA.
Mongolia	Ministry of Forests and Timber Industries, Department of Wildlife Management, ULAN BATOR.

Netherlands	Ministerie van Cultuur, Recreatie en Maatschappelyk Werk, Postbus 5406, 2280 HK RIJSWIJK.
Poland	Ministry of Forestry and Woodworking Industries, Department of Nature Conservation, Ul Wawelska 52/54, 00-992 WARSZAWA 54.
Republic of Korea	Ministry of Agriculture and Fisheries, SEOUL.
Romania	Commission of National Monuments, Calea Victoriei, BUCHAREST.
Spain	Instituto Nacional para la Conservation de la Naturaleza, Gran Via de San Francisco 35, MADRID.
Syria	Ministry of Agriculture and Agrarian Reform, DAMASCUS.
Turkey	General Directorate of Forestry, Ministry of Agriculture and Forestry, Adakale Sokak No. 85, Kadatepe. T–ANKARA.
Yugoslavia	Federal Secretariat for Foreign Trade, BELGRADE.

In addition to the international and national conventions concerning the trade and traffic in wildlife there are also internationally accepted regulations concerning the transport of these creatures by air. Known as the I.A.T.A. controls and details of dimensions, materials and form of construction can be had from any airline which is a member of the International Air Traffic Association (I.A.T.A. for short).

Briefly, however, in respect of transport of birds, the transport crate is of solid construction, usually plywood, with a wire front covered by hessian sacking to allow a free flow of air across the front while offering visual seclusion and avoiding stress to the birds. Dependent on journey time there may also have to be provision for food and/or water, with a false floor, usually of wire, if there is any likelihood of a build-up of droppings, which must in any event fall on any absorbent-type litter. Some countries, however, have a prohibition on the use of litter made from woodshavings, straw or similar material, so this point must be borne in mind.

Figure 7. **Transport Box for Birds**

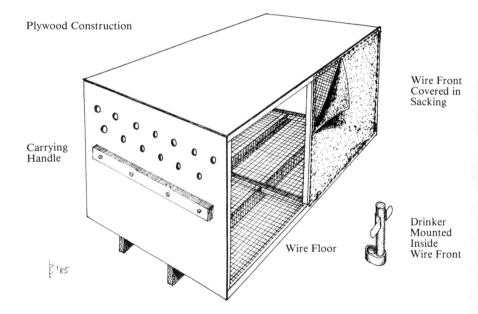

Plywood Construction

Carrying Handle

Wire Front Covered in Sacking

Wire Floor

Drinker Mounted Inside Wire Front

Chapter 3
Ornithological Descriptions

The following Chapter covers the description of each Species within their Families and includes Distribution Maps and Illustrations wherever possible.

Harlequin Quail

Chapter 3.1

Tetraonidae I
(The Grouse)

This is a family of six Genera, comprising eighteen species. Gruson quotes sixteen species but I have treated the Red Grouse as a full species and not a sub-species of the Willow Grouse, because of the substantial differences in plumage, colouration and totally separate geographical location. The Pinnated Grouse are treated as two species.

The species described are:—

1.1	**Black Billed Capercaillie**	1.10	**Siberian Spruce Grouse**
1.2	**Capercaillie**	1.11	**Blue Grouse**
1.3	**Black Grouse**	1.12	**Hazel Grouse**
1.4	**Caucasian Black Grouse**	1.13	**Chinese Hazel Grouse**
1.5	**Ptarmigan**	1.14	**Ruffed Grouse**
1.6	**Red Grouse**	1.15	**Greater Pinnated Grouse**
1.7	**Whitetailed Ptarmigan**	1.16	**Lesser Pinnated Grouse**
1.8	**Willow Grouse**	1.17	**Sharptailed Grouse**
1.9	**Canadian Spruce Grouse**	1.18	**Sage Grouse**

The only known extermination within historic times is the Heath Hen or Eastern Pinnated Grouse which was last recorded in 1932. This was the nominate race of the 'Prairie Chicken'. Most birds are distinctively 'lek' species; that is, during the breeding season the males gather on what are often traditional 'leking' grounds displaying together. The females are attracted to these breeding displays and when stimulated seek mating with a male before returning to their respective nest sites.

In aviculture this family is not widely kept and provides many challenges. Also, some species in fact have never been kept at all, and generally speaking it can be said that this family is the most demanding of all.

Of the seventeen species of Grouse, eight are **Palearctic** and seven **Nearctic**, with two being **Holearctic**. In the case of the Capercaillie however, repeated attempts have been made, and are being made, to introduce the species to North America — with limited, if any, success. Whether this exercise is wise is another matter, of course.

All Grouse species are basically from the North Temperate, Boreal and Arctic regions; southerly distributions are progressively confined to the higher montane habitats.

Black Billed Capercaillie

Species: **BLACK BILLED CAPERCAILLIE**   **1.1**
              Tetrao parvirostris (Bonaparte 1856)

Description Roughly the same size as the Capercaillie, perhaps only marginally smaller, this species, like its counterpart, can only be described as magnificent, especially the cock birds.

As the name implies, this species has a black colouration of both upper and lower mandibles which are all the more noticeable when the bird is calling, exposing the pink of the mouth and tongue. The bill is smaller than that of the Capercaillie.

The general background colouration of cock birds is dark, ranging from blacks to light and dark greys with slight rust tinting on the throat, wings and back. The legs are fully feathered and are lightish grey. There is a white shoulder mark, also white markings on the wings and around the upper tail fan. Above the eye is the usual red eye wattle and under the chin a feathered beard. The hen is markedly smaller, generally reddish brown with black feather barring, overall being darker above, tending to greyish fawn below.

Characteristics and Behaviour   A heavy flyer like the Capercaillie, the mature cocks appear to spend a lot of time on the ground, seeming almost to prefer walking to flying, often walking from or near their roost to their lekking stand, whilst the females and sub-adult males will more frequently fly.

Autumn and winter are spent on the feeding grounds, but with the onset of spring, sexual activity, involving calling and display on the lek, increasingly takes up the time of the cocks, either in securing their territory as with mature adults, or with challenging by sub-adults.

Habitat   The nominate race of this Grouse lives almost exclusively in the Larch forests of Asiatic USSR among a shrub layer of bracken, bilberry and, to the south of their range, also rhododendron. There tends to be a winter migration out of the mountainous areas and into river valleys and flood plains, but always within the Larch forests. The only exception to this is the sub-species *T.p. kamtchatkensis* which lives solely within the birch forests of that region.

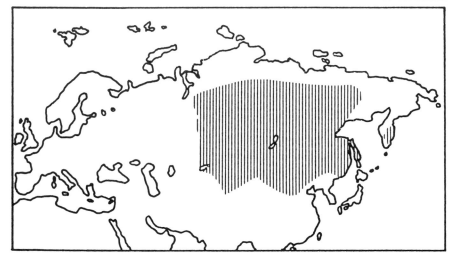

BLACK BILLED CAPERCAILLIE *(Tetrao parvirostris)*   1.1

Food   Apart from the sub-species mentioned above which utilises the shoots and buds of birches, the Black Billed Capercaillie lives on buds and twigs of the Larch *(Larix gmelini)*, blueberries, cranberries, rosehips and the pupae and eggs of forest ants.

Voice   According to Dr. Andreev of the USSR the song of this species is much louder than that of the Capercaillie. There are two song types used by the cock birds. Both are apparently a rythmical clicking, either a vibrating click similar to the *(track)* sound of the Capercaillie, or a simple click akin to the *(tack)* of the other species, and when uttered it sounds like a *'tack-track-tack-tack'* then *'tr-r-rack'* lasting usually around 10 seconds but often about six seconds. During calm weather this sound carries over long distances (up to 500m) and can last from half an hour to an hour.

Display   As with most Forest Grouse there is a wing beating display which Dr. Andreev describes as having little sound effect but rather more visual effect. The purpose is both for display and attack. Flight distances vary from 5–20 metres but only a few centimetres off the ground as a rule. The intensity of this behaviour increases with onset of darkness and might be stimulated by the possibility of intruders more imagined than seen!

Where males meet on the boundaries of their territory they proceed with a ritual stance, neck extended upwards, while maintaining their song. As the confrontation between males develops, often in the absence of the females, there is much bowing and then the birds set about each other with outstretched wings. Serious fights can, in fact, occur.

A most significant and important feature is the outspread tail fan with the white spots facing forward. These are highly distinctive, whereas the underside of the tail coverts is quite a dark colour, unlike that of the Capercaillie which is blotched. On the lek the master cock is noticeable by his greater activity and almost total lack of under tail markings, presumably an indication of increasing age.

The vocalisation of this species is not as extensive as that of the Capercaillie, but the white feather patterns are highly significant and indicate a greater reliance on 'body language' than is the case with the Capercaillie.

Breeding   Little is known on this subject but one may presume that Black Billed Capercaillie are similar in most respects with the Capercaillie. Clutch sizes are probably the same.

Aviculture   So far as I can establish this bird has not been kept in aviculture.

Sub-species   Only one described sub-species is known, the Kamchatka Capercaillie — *Tetrao parvirostris kamchatkensis*, an isolated population living exclusively in the Birch Forests and being the most easterly located Capercaillie.

Distribution   Entirely an Asiatic species, almost exclusively in the USSR, but with a small population in North Eastern China. There is a substantial geographical overlap with the Capercaillie to the west, but owing to habitat preferences both species are not frequently found occupying the same area.

Species: CAPERCAILLIE   1.2
              Tetrao urogallus (Linnaeus)
Description The size of a turkey and unquestionably the largest
              Grouse, it would be no exaggeration to say that the
              Capercaillie is a most singularly distinctive species in
              numerous ways. Apart from the cock bird's enormous
              size this species is one of only two species of bird to be
              universally known by the original name in the Gaelic

language, the other being the Ptarmigan. As a Scot myself it is only natural to be proud of this fact. The name is derived from two Gaelic words 'Capull Coille' meaning 'Horse of the Forest'.

The Capercaillie has one further claim to fame. It is most probably the first successful re-introduction of any species of bird in an area from which they had been previously exterminated by Man. This event took place in Scotland and after a few attempts achieved a success beyond all expectations; so much so that we in Scotland have what may well be the only rapidly expanding population of Capercaillie anywhere at this time.

Throughout the Capercaillie's distribution the species is associated with coniferous forest and is especially found in association with the Scots Pine *(Pinus sylvestris)*, although a population in Finland appears to have adapted to associating with Norway spruce *Picea abies)*. The sexes are strikingly dimorphic with the hen being beautifully marked for camouflage. Overall the impression is one of fawns and brown barring; the breast is chestnut with wing and back barring being darker. Legs in both sexes are fully feathered and the beaks are light horn coloured.

Cock birds are about one third larger than hens. The head and neck are blackish grey with a chest of dark green. The under parts are black with faint grey markings. Birds from the north eastern parts of the Capercaillie's range are, however, nearly white on the belly, grading to grey at the vent. Wing coverts and back are rufous with rump and tail feathers dark grey to black. When fanning the tail in display and seen from the rear there are quite distinctive white markings and it seems that these are all the more noticeable in older birds. In fact on any given lek it is possible to identify individual birds by their tail markings.

Cock birds have a noticeable tuft of feathers on what might be described as their chin.

My first and lasting impression of Capercaillie was early on a frosty morning disturbing 3-4 cock birds at their roost in a group of Birch trees from which they launched themselves, crashing through the branches to get airborne and creating a tremendous racket in so doing. Perhaps I gave them a surprise, but it was nothing to the one they gave me.

Characteristics and Behaviour   The hen is unmistakeably 'Grouse' but the cock is only describable with a string of superlatives. Firstly he is the biggest, being quite enormous. The Scots and Irish did not call him Capull Coille − Horse of the Forest − for nothing. Secondly, the leking songs sound like the popping corks of a champagne party. As would be expected of a large bird the flight, although fast, is heavy and deliberate. In cold weather the cocks find it easier to become airborne by launching themselves from a tall tree — often a pine but also from mature birches high up on a hill or valley side.

Habitat   Generally Capercaillie are reliant on a single tree species, the Scots pine, which for a game bird is something of a handicap taste wise, as was fairly succinctly put to me by a forestry trapper when I enquired how best to prepare Caper. The reply was "carry the bird into the forest taking a spade in the other hand. After ten minutes stop and dig a pit in the ground about one metre deep, placing the bird in it and then filling the hole again, carefully covering the location with pine needles. Stand up, blindfold yourself, turn around several times, take twenty paces forward then turn a few more times, take off the blindfold and if you have any sense you will forget you even shot the bird!" Specialising in eating pine buds and needles does nothing to commend their flavour. Other foods are eaten, such as various berries and leaves of ground plants like Bilberry. During the breeding season a lot of insects, grubs and so forth are taken, particularly ants. This insect diet is vital to the growing chicks, especially the young cocks whose growth rate is exceptionally rapid in the first weeks and months of life.

For everyone there is a personal perception of nature, and to my mind the Pine forests of the Northlands without the Capercaillie would be like a body without a heart, the life all gone. In these modern times of 'optimum yields' and 'cost effective' harvesting we too often lose sight of the natural scheme of things. Large areas of even aged conifers are of little value to much of forest wildlife. This is especially the case for Capercaillie who need large and small trees, open and close grown trees, undisturbed leking grounds; in fact, all the things the men with the slide rules can never comprehend.

The Capercaillie is part of the Forest cycle and rhythm, as are the ants and their hills of needles. We in Scotland have been over the precipice with Capercaillie having plundered our formerly vast Pine forests, leaving very little by 1800 and virtually none by 1900. Our last Capercaillie disappeared during the late eighteenth century. However, birds and eggs were brought to Scotland from Sweden by landowners who were also replanting some of the Forest lands, so that the birds rapidly re-established themselves until the next onslaught on the forests during the First World War. After this period strenuous efforts were made to re-afforest Scotland's now bare mountains and valleys, with the resulting rapid re-establishment and expansion of Capercaillie, which seem to be far more adaptable than they are given credit for, as they are adapting to non-Pine tree species including Larches, Firs, and Spruces, which are more frequently planted on the wetter western areas of Scotland. The magnitude of this adaptation can be gauged from the fact that 80% of all re-afforestation now undertaken is using Sitka Spruce *(Picea sitchensis)* — a tree originating from Western North America. The lesson to be learned from this ecological example should be well heeded by all involved in the wildlife field.

Voice   The Hen's call is a fairly simple *'kok'*, repeated with varying frequency. The Cock's call, or to be generous, song, is varied and

CAPERCAILLIE *(Tetrao urogallus)*   **1.2**

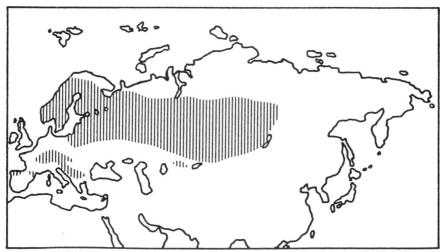

serves two purposes mainly: courtship display and territorial aggression. Described variously as belching, popping corks and pouring liquid from a bottle, but most frequently as *'tack, tack, tack-tack'* similar to rapping a ring on a wooden table.

Display   As it is a leking species, cock birds are to be found on station with a master cock holding court. These leking displays are very vigorous and active, attended by the females who usually mate with the master cock.

Sub-species   The original *T.u. caledonicus* was exterminated by 1770 but there is a population in the Pyrenees known as *T.u. aquitanicus* and another possibly larger race *T.u. taczanowskii*, others include *T.u. major, T.u. karelicus, T.u. uralensis, T.u. rudolfi.*

Distribution   In many areas of central Europe, particularly Germany, Capercaillie are very much on the decline due partly to destruction of habitat, but one suspects largely due to the practice of shooting master cocks on the lek and the effect this must be having on the vigour of the remaining genetic material.

Attempts are being proposed for re-introduction to Italy with birds from Spain, something everyone hopes will be successful. Re-introduction to Ireland should now be possible. Most of the available area in Northern Scotland is being re-colonised but natural southward expansion to Southern Scotland is prevented by the industrial Midlands. This could be given human assistance as could also attempts in parts of England and Wales.

Species: **BLACK GROUSE**   **1.3**
             Tetrao tetrix (Linnaeus)*

Description Undoubtedly one of the most distinctive species of all the Grouse with the males' overall black colouration and spectacular lyre-shaped tail seen as they wheel around a thicket of scrub before dropping into a clump of heather. Closer inspection reveals the cock bird to have a splendid glossy plumage with fully feathered legs of white, and also a white shoulder patch and a narrow, white, wing bar. The under-tail coverts are also white and very distinctive, especially during the courtship display.

*The genus formerly known as *Lyrurus* now merged with *Tetrao*.

As if the stark contrast between black and white was not enough to satisfy these vain males, during the breeding season they also have startling red eye wattles which seem all the more noticeable set as they are against the black of the head plumage. It is hard to imagine the females belong to the same species with their sombre colour, no unusual tail, and only being about 40 cm in size compared with the males' 53 cm size.

Characteristics and Behaviour   Inclined to fly higher than Red Grouse, although perhaps not quite so fast, although this could be an illusion. Frequently seen cracking and rocketing out of the tree tops, rapidly flying across to trees on the other side of a valley, often with long glides, finally wheeling before a quick flutter to trim for a landing either on the ground or near the top of a Pine or Larch tree in what seems a precarious position.

Not far from my house Blackcock can be seen feeding on Larch buds during the winter. Perching as they do fairly near to the tree's swaying top they occasionally over-reach themselves and have to fly off to another tree. These same trees serve as roosts in cold weather, and in the mornings the birds are quite obviously warming themselves in the early morning sun before flying off in the warmer upper airs to either forage for food or join other birds on the leking grounds.

Early in the breeding season males indulge in leking displays, often of great intensity, involving as many as ten or more cocks. Starting early in the morning, the visual display is accompanied by much vocalisation amongst the cocks; often leks are located first by the sounds coming from them. I saw my first Black Cock lek at the age of 16, and it is as fresh in the memory as when I first saw it. This sight has to be one of nature's 'biggest thrills'. In the autumn there are sporadic and less intense leks with smaller numbers of cock birds.

Habitat   Open and discontinuous forest and forest edges, scrub and adjacent heather moorland. The preferred tree species are Birch, Pine and Larch, with the buds being an attraction. The shrub layer includes Bilberry, Heather, Willows and Juniper. Black Grouse occupy young forest as a transitional species until the tree reaches the thicket stages when their numbers decline, or they relocate to other clear, felled areas when they are replanted.

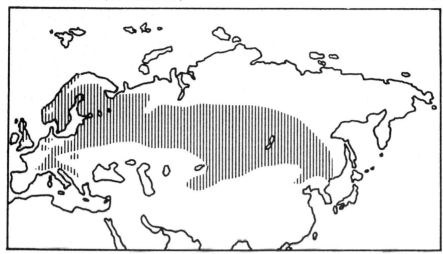

BLACK GROUSE *(Tetrao tetrix)*   1.3

Food   During the winter and spring much use is made of buds of the Pine, Birch and Larch, which does make them unpopular with foresters in Pine areas, especially in newly planted or regenerating areas. Quantities of Bilberry and Heather shoots are also consumed as are insects, grubs, larvae, etc., particularly in the spring.

Voice   The cocks, particularly in the breeding season, indulge in peculiar sorts of cooing and bubbling notes. Ordinarily the call is like a painful sneeze with the hen using a Pheasant like *'kok, kok'* call.

Display   As mentioned above the males indulge in displays on leking grounds; these seem almost to be mock fights. Leking sites are usually found in forest clearings or hollows. Many are traditional and can be lost during forest operations.

Breeding   The female, known as the Greyhen, and the male have no apparent permanent pair bond or even a temporary one. Greyhens crouch, watching from the sideline as it were as the males display their finery and, when excited, approach the males, soliciting mating which then quickly takes place. When mated the females go off to their respective nests, brooding and rearing their young alone.
   Studies in Sweden by Per Angelstam support the view that brood survival, and hence population fluctuations, is related to population

levels of small rodents. What this means in effect is that as rodents tend to have peaks and troughs in population levels, where these occur at the highest level Grouse species do appear to bring off more young as the attention of predators is otherwise directed to the rodents. From personal observations in the last four years ('76–'80) this does seem to be occurring in my part of the West Highlands of Scotland. As 1980 has been one of the best years for Grouse in this area, with numbers noticeably higher than previously, so too are the rodent and predator populations.

Nest sites are often located at the base of a tree amongst ferns, long heather or under fallen trees or even branches which can provide seclusion. Clutch sizes vary but range from six to ten. A single clutch is laid in late April or early May. The eggs are buff coloured with reddish brown markings, mainly spots or blotches of varying size.

Aviculture   Very few birds are kept and bred in captivity. The most noticeably successful collection is at Helsinki Zoo in Finland. It is advisable to keep these birds as pinioned specimens otherwise under aviary conditions they will readily break their necks flying fast at the wire. Another successful aviculturalist, Ursula Wilmering in West Germany, keeps her birds in large pens, open-topped and with plenty of natural cover including grasses, shrubs and small trees; these birds are obviously pinioned.

Sub-species   Four sub-species have been described and are as follows:–
1) *Tetrao tetrix baikalensis* (Lorenze 1911). The males dark colouring tends to be tinted with what is described as rufous with glossy green upper parts, and appears to be marginally larger. Distribution is in the main confined to the USSR, neighbouring China, parts of Mongolia and a small population crosses the border into North East China.
2) *Tetrao tetrix mongolicus* (Lönnberg 1904). The male's black brown colouring is of a deeper shade than the nominate form with upper parts a deep blue with a reddish gloss. This race is found in the northern Sinkrang Region of China and across the border into the USSR.
3) *Tetrao tetrix ussuriensis* (Kohts 1911). Males are somewhat similar to *L.t. baikalensis* but tending to a blue-green gloss.
4) *Tetrao tetrix viridannus*. Description not available; Russian distribution.

Black Grouse are also frequently referred to as Black Cock, particularly in the Eastern parts of Scotland and also parts of England. The female of the species being referred to as the Greyhen.

Distribution   Once found generally throughout Central and Northern Europe, except Ireland. The position now is very much one of decline in most areas, except Scotland, where, allowing for population cycles, they seem to be on the increase. Sadly, at the opposite end of the scale, Denmark has shown a rapid post-war decline best described as total disaster. Most of the causes can be associated with habitat destruction and to a lesser extent overhunting.

Species: **CAUCASIAN BLACK GROUSE**   **1.4**
             Tetrao mlokosiewiczi *

Description   Slightly smaller than the Black Grouse which it closely resembles generally. There are, however, some very basic and significant differences. There is no white in the ventral area, this being black. The white shoulder bar is totally absent with only the slightest suggestion of white on the shoulder. The fully feathered legs are white as with the Black Grouse. The hen's tail is rounded, not slightly forked as in the Black Grouse hen. The other distinctive feature is the much longer tail feathers than in the Black Grouse, with only a small curvature to the 4−5 longest feathers which also tend to have a downward angle.

Characteristics and Behaviour   Very similar in fact to the Black Grouse in most respects. However, this species has not been studied to any extent and much information is still lacking.

Habitat   Again information is rather scanty, but what is known is that these birds are found at fairly high elevations in the Caucasus or Alpine meadows and in scrubland in the higher valleys.

Food   This is more or less as for the Black Grouse, and like the other species a valuable addition to the diet, especially in the breeding season, include grubs, insects and their larvae.

*The genus known as *Lyrurus* now merged with *Tetrao*.

Caucasian Black Grouse

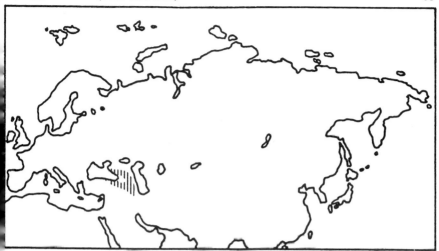

CAUCASIAN BLACK GROUSE *(Tetrao mlokosiewiczi)*   **1.4**

Voice   Believed to be virtually the same as for Black Grouse, but no record of information on this point is definitely available.

Display   Here there is an appreciable difference with Black Grouse as, firstly, the spectacular ventral feathers are absent, making for less of a contrast; also, whereas in the Black Grouse the 'lyre' shaped tail feathers are out and downward, this species raises its long tail feathers upwards at an acute angle while pointing forward with the neck and head.

Breeding   The same as for the Black Grouse.

Aviculture   There are no records of this species being kept or bred in captivity so far as I have been able to ascertain.

Sub-species   There are none.

Distribution   Confined to the Caucasus Mountains exclusively with populations in each of the countries bordering on this area, these being Turkey, Iran and the USSR. Because of the isolated location of this species so far South, and located as it is amongst very high mountains, it is tempting to suggest that the Caucasian Black Grouse a relic population which formally had a much greater distribution during cooler climatic periods. Furthermore, it may just possibly be that this species could be the ancestral stock of the Black Grouse which has developed a more advanced and effective reproductive leking display through better colour contrasts of white and black feathers. A further indication that this might be the case is the less prominent red eye wattle of the Caucasian Black Grouse as compared with the Black Grouse, and also the absence of white wing bars.

If one in fact looks at the races and sub-species of Black Grouse as they radiate away from the Caucasus, particularly to the East, the birds become all the more colourful which, in the case of the cocks, one might suppose may give them the edge over their progressively more dowdy counterparts.

Species: PTARMIGAN   1.5
                Lagopus mutus (Montiss)

Description This is the Grouse of the high arctic and highest moun-
             tain ranges throughout the Northern Hemisphere. This
             is referred to in North America as the Rock Ptarmigan.
             Plumage in winter is identical to that of the Willow
             Grouse, being all white with black tail primaries and
             also a black eye stripe from the mandibles through to
             the eyes. The bill size in this species is noticeably less
             stout than that of the Willow Grouse. During the
             summer the wing primaries and secondaries remain
             white white the upper parts are greyish-buff, more
             rufous in the Hen. Legs and toes are fully feathered
             being white all year round. The Cock has the typically
             prominent red eye wattle during the breeding season.

Characteristics and Behaviour Typically the Cocks take territory
during the spring using vantage points from which they call and fly
off to drive away intruders.

As with all members of this genera Cocks have a song flight varying in height from just above ground to over 50 metres. These flights
are characterised by a rapid wing beat upwards, usually followed by
a dipping glide. While normally paired, Cocks can have more than
one hen within their territory.

Flights between equally aggressive males often develop into serious
confrontations with bill biting and wing beating.

Habitat Found exclusively in Alpine and Tundra areas, rocky and
peaty terrain with the short vegetation typical of these areas.

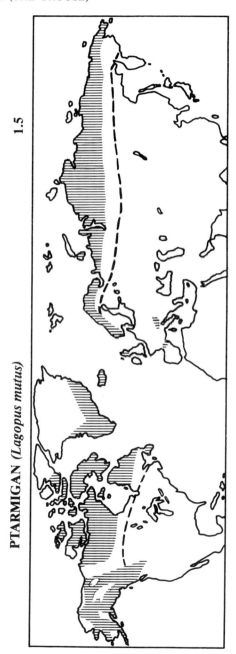

1.5

PTARMIGAN *(Lagopus mutus)*

Voice   The two distinctive calls are either a croaking *'uk uk'* or a grating *'karikirrkrrkrr'*.

Display   Like Willow Grouse in many respects and nothing spectacular. Both species have a 'low profile' involving neck swelling with short calls and running up to the Hen with tail tilted towards her while extending a wing away from her.

Breeding   Having paired off, Hens rely on the Cocks for alarm warnings and devote their activities to the tending of the brood, very solicitous of them.

Aviculture   A few enthusiasts do keep these birds in North America and Europe, but they require considerable attention.

Sub-species   11 quoted by Johnsgard from North America but frankly these seem unwarranted as all species with extensive ranges have a range of variations that hardly justify sub-species status. This is not a criticism of Johnsgard. He only refers to them; I don't intend to bother.

Distribution   This species has a circumpolar distribution wherever suitable habitat occurs.

Species: RED GROUSE   1.6
             Lagopus scoticus (Latham)

Description This species of Grouse is restricted to the British Isles with its greatest strength of numbers in Scotland and also Ireland. Some authorities place Red Grouse as a sub-species of Willow Grouse, but this seems quite wrong and if accepted would mean considerable review of taxanomical criteria and re-classification of many species of bird in numerous genera.

   As with all species in the *Lagopus* genera the sexes are not obviously dimorphic, unlike other Grouse. This is probably due to numerous factors including occupation of habitat with limited cover dictating the need for the muted plumage, affording greatest benefits for camouflage.

   The name Red Grouse in English is very accurate as the summer plumage is a deep red brown with the prominent red eye wattle. Both in Scotland and Ireland this bird's name in Gaelic is 'Fraoch' meaning 'Heather Cock', which is also very accurate as this species is entirely associated with Heather *(Calluna)* upon which these Grouse depend for food. Winter plumage differs only slightly in tone and unlike the Willow Grouse, Red Grouse never moult into a white feathering, not even partially. Birds from Ireland appear to be darker with an almost black chest and belly feathering.

The legs are fully feathered in greyish white all year round. In flight the Red Grouse is very fast, and it needs to be as it must contend with the Peregrine Falcon as one of its major predators. In very severe weather birds will descend from the mountains to farmland, but prolonged exclusion from Heather reduces their capability for survival.

Characteristics and Behaviour Of all the Grouse, perhaps the Red Grouse presents the Hunter with the toughest challenge, speeding past or just over as they do with great elan. I suspect more Grouse are sworn at than shot at for this reason. Such are the challenges associated with this species that in the United Kingdom (particularly Scotland) whole rural communities are to a great extent reliant on the income generated from the shooting on Grouse moorland.

With the combined factors of territoriality and hierarchy the world for the cock birds is a fairly ruthless place. In periods of high population the least aggressive cocks are so entirely and effectively excluded from holding territory, and therefore having access to adequate food, that they simply die. During late summer and early winter birds move around in family parties which eventually break up slowly through natural mortality or predation until by the spring the situation returns to strictly territorial pairs. In this the *Lagopus* genera appear to differ from other grouse. They do not lek in the accepted sense, and appear to be fairly stable as pairs.

Food and Habitat Very strictly a bird associated with a single plant species and even the age and hence the quality of Heather will dictate population levels, distribution and success rates. The preferred locations are short, young Heather for feeding and longer, rank, old Heather in which to nest. Regardless of daily consumption one bird prior to roosting needs one square metre from which to feed. They

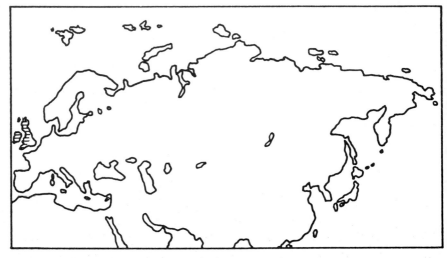

RED GROUSE *(Lagopus scoticus)*   **1.6**

pick up mineral grit also and this assists in the breakdown of the heather in the gizzard.

Assuming reasonable weather during the winter, with the attendant higher survival rate and lack of dessication by the wind of the heather shoots, successful rearing of broods is by no means assured if bad spring weather reduces or delays insects hatching. These insects are vital for the high protein intake needed by the chicks and poults.

Voice   There are two main calls, the simple *'kok-kok-kok'* or the perhaps better known *'go back-go back-go back'*. On open hillside or moorland these calls travel well and allow the cock birds to space themselves out throughout the available territories.

Display   As with all members of the *Lagopus* Grouse the display element is not so highly developed as it is with the Forest Grouse, and leking as a feature is absent. Great emphasis is placed on the call when birds are displaying on their respective territories, and the 'flutter jump' of the forest species is developed into long but rapid upward flight before dipping back down. Physical confrontations can and do take place, most often on the ground but to a lesser extent in the air. These conflicts between cocks can lead to serious fights when conducted between well matched birds.

Breeding   Females, paired off with territorial males, seek out a site with suitable cover — often in rank Heather, under a small Willow or in Bog Myrtle — where a clutch of usually 4–6 buff coloured eggs with tan or dark brown blotches is laid and brooded by the female. The male continues to hold and defend the territory.

After hatching, the broods are soon on the wing and stay together as a group, only breaking up very much later in the year. Success of the young is very varied and heavily reliant on the quality of Heather eaten by the female during the previous winter, the absence of late snow or heavy rains, and an adequate supply of insect larvae followed by good quality young heather in sufficient quantity.

Aviculture   Pioneer work in captivity was done by Adam Watson and Robert Moss of the Institute of Terrestial Ecology in Scotland. The system they evolved is based on hutches raised off the ground with wire floors incorporated. For their purposes of study and experiment this is ideal but it is unsuited for public display. However, the principles can be easily adapted, but the birds in my view must be pinioned for when startled they rocket forward and break their necks more often than not.

Sub-species   There are none.

Distribution   Restricted to heathland at varying elevations within the British Isles including Ireland, but absent from most of England now. Most commonly found in Scotland wherever there is Heather.

Species: **WHITETAILED PTARMIGAN**   **1.7**
                 Lagopus leucurus (Richardson)
Description Distinguished from all other Ptarmigan by its permanently white tail and wings. The remaining colouration is buff brown with barring and mottling of black and dark brown during the summer. In winter this bird is totally white excepting the bill, eyes and claws.

Characteristics and Behaviour   Territorially similar to the other Ptarmigan. Oddly, however, hens also have eye wattles although they are not so noticeable. After pairing, behaviour continues to be along similar lines.

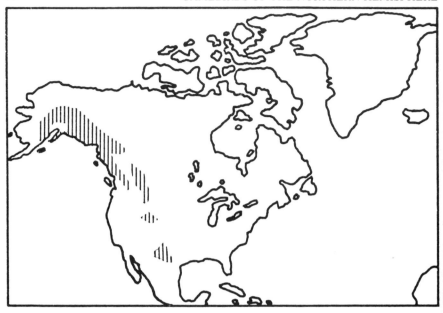

WHITETAILED PTARMIGAN *(Lagopus leucurus)*   **1.7**

Habitat   High Montane areas above the tree line, but Braun suggests that there is an important association with Alpine Willows and invariably very rocky sites avoiding boggy areas with high vegetation.

Voice   Various calls are used, variously described as *duk-duk-Daak-duk-duk* or *Daak-daak-duk-duk-duk*.

Display   This species has not been studied very much and it would seem from what little information is available that White Tailed Ptarmigan are fairly similar to others in their postures and attitudes in display.

Breeding   Around 4–8 eggs, sometimes more, are laid in areas of rock terrain associated with suitable plants as food resources.

Aviculture   I can find no record so far of captive breeding.

Sub-species   Four sub-species are noted by Johnsgaard.

Distribution   Western North America from Alaska South through Canada, with outlying isolated groups in Wyoming, Colorado and just into New Mexico.

Species: **WILLOW GROUSE**   **1.8**
Lagopus lagopus (Linnaeus)

Description Slightly larger than the Red Grouse to which it is closely related. In North America this species is also known as Willow Ptarmigan. Unlike the Red Grouse this species has a winter plumage which is pure white, excepting the tail primaries which are black, as is the eye area. Breeding and summer plumage of the cock is a warm, rufous brown with white wing primaries and secondaries; the belly vent and legs are also white. In the hen, at this season only, the wing has the white of the cock and the underparts are light fawn with dark brown barring. As with all the *lagopus* species the cock has very prominent red eye wattles during the breeding season. Flight is very rapid, both in terms of wing beats and time taken to cover any given distance.

Characteristics and Behaviour The most dominant cocks hold the best territories and their hens have the highest survival rate of chicks, with less dominant birds progressively pushed on to poorer habitat. During severe weather these birds will move down to lower ground but they are unable to survive for very long without their normal habitat. They are nevertheless remarkably resilient and make use of snow holes in which to seek shelter from all but the severest weather.

Habitat Found mainly at lower elevations than the Ptarmigan, usually amongst willow, birch and juniper scrub, open Forest and Heather moorland.

Voice Similar to Red Grouse but also with an additional call phrase *'ow...ow'* followed by a slight pause then *'Kowk-ok-ok-ok-ok'*. Also, when startled, *'gobak-gobak-gobak'*.

Display Apart from territorial calls from their own 'patch', which serve to space out territories, little active display is indulged in; males are repelled and a female attracted in.

Breeding Pairs having taken territory which is defended by the cock, the female locates her nest in a clump of ground cover, lays her clutch of 4−7 eggs and incubates these by herself. During late summer and autumn family parties stay together, breaking up during the winter, usually due to fatalities. There is no certain indication

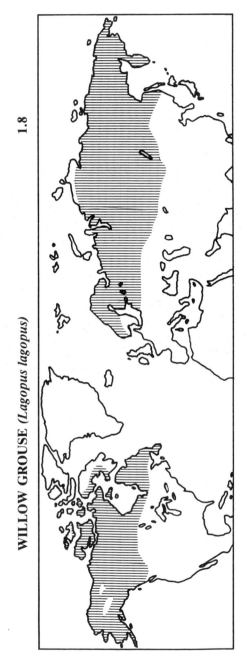

1.8

WILLOW GROUSE (*Lagopus lagopus*)

that pairs remain mated, but in all probability birds successful on one territory any one year are likely to resume their relationship with one or both partners the following season, as is probably the case with Red Grouse.

Aviculture Perhaps the person with greatest experience is Robert Moss, who regularly breeds these birds in Scotland and has also hybridised them with Red Grouse, producing fertile hybrids, back-crossed both ways.

Sub-species Seven quoted by Johnsgard but there seems to be no justification in some of these.

Distribution This species has a circumpolar distribution from Norway in the west through to Greenland in the east.

Species: **CANADIAN SPRUCE GROUSE**   **1.9**
                Dendragopus canadensis (Linnaeus)

Description A beautiful Forest Grouse of North America. The cock is heavily vermiculated with an underlying blue grey ground colour, each feather black barred over most of the head, neck, back and breast where there are white bars rather than black. The chin, lower throat and tail feathers are black; there are white feathers below the eye with a suggestion of a collar, and white central etching to the wing secondaries. The overall tone of the wings is somewhat darker. Normally one has strong reservations over the sub-specific status of many species but if ever there was a clear case for it this is to be seen in the Franklin Spruce Grouse which is toned strongly dark brown. Cocks have strong red eye wattles during the breeding season. Hens are cryptically coloured in similar tones to their respective cocks.

Characteristics and Behaviour Cocks tend to be spaced out on home ranges of varying sizes with a core home range which is vigorously defended to some extent, but most importantly serves as a display location. There seems to be some evidence that paired hens outside the breeding season are faithful to their natural territory, although while rearing their broods they move to suitable feeding

territory which may or may not be synonymous with the general
territory.

This Grouse has a very strongly defined and remarkable 'flutter
jump' involving an upward flight of some 4–5 metres using rapid
wing beats. Their return to ground culminates in the hard slapping
backwards and together of the wings twice, making loud claps,
after which the bird glides down to the ground, rock or log before
repeating the display. The wing clap occurs about one metre before
alighting.

When displaying, cocks inflate their neck feathers, holding their
tail upright and revealing white tipped feathers pointing in all directions while the tail can be switched sideways. They strut up to the
hens with preliminary bowing followed by a typical wing droop.
There are other elements also, making up a complex display in cocks.

Habitat   Dense coniferous forests across the Northern Boreal North
American Forests, littered with moss and lichen-covered fallen logs.

CANADIAN SPRUCE GROUSE *(Dendragopus canadensis)*   **1.9**

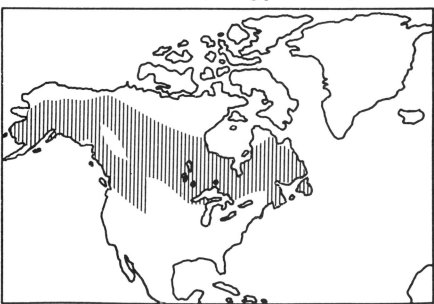

Food   Much use is made of Pine and Spruce needles and buds, also Blueberries, Cranberries and Juniper. Young birds also rely on the Vaccinium species but use all available insects and their larvae.

Voice   The breeding call has been defined as a low hoot, while aggressive calls include variously *'kaee' rrr'* and *'kruk'*. Hens have a soft *'pit-pit-pit'* when disturbed.

Breeding   Clutch sizes vary between 5–9 eggs, averaging 6–7 eggs. The hen incubates on its own for 21 days. Although cocks are seen accompanying broods they are not recorded as taking an active part in their care.

Aviculture   So far Canadian aviculturalists are the main propagators, although some birds are also successfully kept by enthusiasts on the East Coast of the United States.

Sub-species   Originally referred to as *Canachites canadesnis* by Linnaeus. The American Ornithological Union identify four sub-species but in my view only *Dendragopus canadensia franklinii* seems valid.

Distribution   Found throughout Canada among the conifer forests from the Atlantic to the Pacific. Also found in border states of the United States with suitable habitats.

Species: SIBERIAN SPRUCE GROUSE   1.10
Dendragopus falcipennis (Hartlaub)

Description   Although no doubt familiar to the indigenous population in the eastern Asiatic regions of what is now the USSR, parts of China around the Amur river, Sakhalin Island, Kamchatka and areas opposite Alaska, it is not well known to science. The blackish plumage is marked with a white pattern similar to the Canadian Spruce Grouse. Wing primaries are unusually shaped with the leading edge being longest, sharply inclined backwards, while the tail is elongated and somewhat narrower than usual.

Ordinarily I would defer to anything Ingemar Hjorth has to say on Grouse but not his attempt to substitute the name 'Okhotsian Grouse', his argument being that there is a risk in tieing the species to a conifer that does not comprise it's whole diet. The logical extension of this is to then also change the name of the Canadian Spruce Grouse which utilizes large proportions of Pine and Larch in its diet. I prefer to stick with the existing common name as one can hardly pronounce 'Okhotsian' anyway.

The throat, cheek and upper breast of cocks are black, and the feet are heavily covered by grey feathering. Hens are basically similar, if a little smaller, and are without the white eye, ear and throat stripe, and the prominent eye wattles.

Characteristics and Behaviour   Not a great deal is known and published, but there is a wing beat display similar to the Canadian species in cock birds, which also distend their neck feathers while tail fanning, usually from a log or stump from which, while indulging in the flutter jump, a sharp call is made. Perching among branches in the lower canopy is common, especially during severe night temperatures. Small alitudinal migrations also occur.

Habitat   Mainly mature conifer forest of mixed species of Ajan Spruce, Firs and Dahurian Larch. The ground flora are mosses, Blueberries and other vaccinium species, also Ferns.

SIBERIAN SPRUCE GROUSE *(Dendragopus falcipennis)*   **1.10**

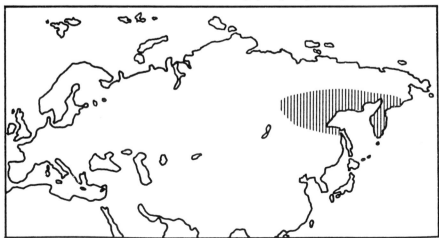

Food   Very little is available on this subject by any authors but it is quite reasonable to assume a similar if not identical diet to the Canadian species.

Breeding   The cocks have a strutting display with tail feature and wing drooping while tails flick open repeatedly. Stimulated hens fly in, usually from an observation perch in a tree, prior to soliciting copulation.

Voice   Two calls are described, a single or more often double *'click'* likened to that of the Black Billed Capercaillie, uttered with its mouth open, and a cooing whistle rising in pitch, followed or preceded usually by a hissing sound, but not always.

Aviculture   There seems to be no record of this species in captivity.

Sub-species   Owing to restricted distributions it is doubtful that there could be any.

Distribution   The Taiga and Boreal Forests of the remote north east regions of Asia, mainly within the USSR.

Species: BLUE GROUSE   1.11
            Dendragopus obscurus (Say)
Description This is my personal favourite amongst North American
            Grouse, and is to me highly suggestive of Capercaillie
            when displaying. Cock birds have a muted colouration
            with different geographical populations varying in tone.
            At one extreme there is the blue grey of the Dusky race,
            having a beautiful broad grey blue margin, while at the
            other extreme it is brown grey with grey black on the
            outer tail fan and lighter grey on the under parts.
                Hens of all races are mottled brown, chestnut and
            grey, cryptically coloured for ideal camouflage on the
            forest floor. Very slight evidence of eye wattles can be
            seen in hens, but these are most pronounced in the cocks
            which also have a red throat patch which is exposed
            when distended.

Behaviour and Characteristics   Cocks are polygamous and highly territorial, having a fairly sophisticated display used to attract and perform in front of hens. There is a display flight, consisting of rapidly rising, followed by a gliding turn sometimes with a loud wing clap before landing. There is a throat patch called the **apterum** which when displaying is exposed, showing the white down contrasting with the red muscle-covered skin tissue.

Habitat   Mature coniferous forests with openings. Ground flora includes low shrub layers of vaccinium berry bearing species, mosses and ferns. Temperature extremes in the north of this species' range create altitudinal migration to easier foraging areas at these periods.

BLUE GROUSE *(Dendragopus obscurus)*   1.11

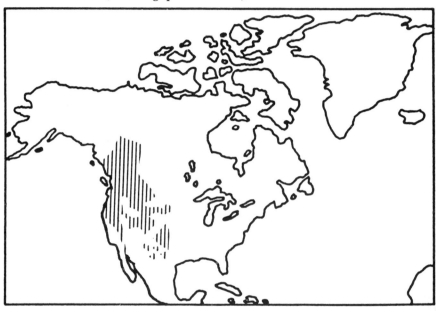

Food   Conifer needles, including Pines, Firs and Hemlocks to a very large extent, also insects and larvae.

Voice   *'Hooting'* is how this bird's call is most frequently described. A series of repetitive *'Hoots'* is produced either from a branch in the mid canopy of trees or in secluded brush and undergrowth.

Breeding   The cocks take no interest in the hens after breeding, nor in the resulting broods. Clutch sizes vary between 6–10 eggs requiring 26 days for incubation. Nests are usually located at the base of a tree, under fallen logs or brushwood.

Sub-species Eight sub-species including the nominate race are identified by the A.O.U., but apart from the *Dendragopus obscurus obscurus* (Duskey Blue Grouse) and the *Dendragopus obscurus richardsonii* (Richardsons Blue Grouse) I fail to see enough justification for all of these in fact, although two more may be valid.

Distribution From South Eastern Alaska and adjacent areas of Canada southwards to Southern Californian mountain ranges.

Species: HAZEL GROUSE 1.12
Bonasa bonasia*

Description Both sexes are cryptically coloured and fairly similar. The overall appearance consists of a greyish crown, head, beck, back and tail with fine chestnut markings around the head. The tail has an outer margin of white above which is a broad band of black broken across the middle. Feathering across the flanks, chest and ventral areas is generally chestnut marginated by light grey or white. In the hen this colour combination is reversed and smaller. Present in the cocks but not in hens is a black ear mark, chin tuft and throat with a white eye stripe running across and down just above and behind.

Characteristics and Behaviour This is a forest Grouse but not a lekking species. Cocks do take and hold territory which they share monogamously with the Hen at least during the breeding season. While the cocks are fairly faithful to their territory, hens may well move around or even off in search of suitable food while rearing their broods in the initial stages. After fledging however, hens are recorded as being on territory with the cocks.

Cocks will actively pursue intruding birds, though this only rarely results in fighting which, when it occurs, takes the form of wing beating and hierarchical body language. Short upward flutter jumps are frequently performed, with loud wing beats the sound of which seems to stimulate a response from neighbouring cocks.

Habitat The name is a little misleading as very little Hazel is found throughout the species range and it is often absent altogether. Primarily a bird of mixed conifer and mixed conifer/deciduous forest

*The genus formerly was known as *Testrastes*, now merged with *Bonasa*.

— if anything favouring Spruce, particularly during the thicket stage and just after.

Food   Shoots, buds and needles of local conifer species, also Willow Birch and Hazel. The usual berry plants (Vaccinimum) are also important.

HAZEL GROUSE *(Bonasa bonasia)*   1.12

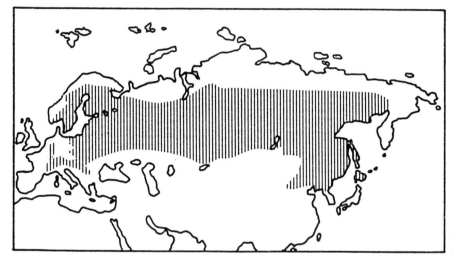

Breeding   The cocks during autumnal behaviour have a strange whistle delivered from a tree branch in mid canopy, in a somewhat hunched attitude similar to a roosting posture. Cocks circle the soliciting hen with the usual wing trailing and the tail is also fanned and spread in the same plane as the wing, showing plumage colour to greatest effect. Additionally both birds indulge in left-right head twisting prior to copulation when the cock holds the hen's less well developed crest with the mandibles.

Voice   Apart from the whistling mentioned above by cocks they also have a repetitive chirp used when moving forward on the ground to another bird responding to the whistle call. Hens also have a chirp call somewhat lower in level used both in response to the cock and as a location call for the brood during foraging.

Aviculture   Recently a number of aviculturalists in Germany (Scherziner, Aschenbrener and Wilmering) have been successful with this species. One valuable lesson learned is that if cocks are within hearing range of each other, although separated, they can become so aggressive that in frustration they can injure or kill the sitting hen. A large and well landscaped aviary is required, with sufficient shrub cover to protect the hen when sitting.

Sub-species   A number of 4−8 is referred to in literature, but the validity, or at least the necessity, for them, is doubtful.

Distribution   Central and Northern Europe eastwards to Siberia, China and Korea.

Species: **CHINESE HAZEL GROUSE**   **1.13**
                Bonasa sewerzowi*

Description   Basically similar in general respects to the Hazel Grouse, but considerably more heavily black barred, and overall more dark in appearance with dark brown from the crown, neck, back and tail.

Characteristics and Behaviour   It is extremely difficult to obtain any detailed information on this species and in the absence of studies

CHINESE HAZEL GROUSE *(Bonasa sewerzowi)*   **1.13**

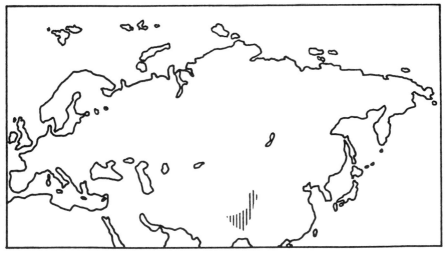

*The genus formerly known as *Testrastes*, now merged with *Bonasa*.

it would be reasonable to suppose that this species is very similar in all major respects to the much more common species.

Habitat   Coniferous forests with Tamark larch as well as spruces, birch and willows. There are no hazels in this region at all.

Food   Again in the absence of information to the contrary this must be assumed to be the same in most respects.

Breeding   The same observation as for food must also apply.

Voice   Apparently the same.

Aviculture   Not known to have been kept in captivity.

Sub-species   None.

Distribution   North Central China.

Species: **RUFFED GROUSE**   **1.14**
                 Bonasa umbellus (Linnaeus)

Description The only North American species of this Genus, and showing considerable variation in colouring and barring East to West, North and South. The plumage variables are due to the variations in the tree and shrub layer habitats, which are quite considerable. Generally speaking the ground colour is rather greyish with brown tones, with a broad black sub-terminal tail bar and regular narrow lines also found on the flank and chest bars, with black around the lower edges of the mantle and upper wing coverts. The overall impression is cryptic with both sexes fairly similar except that the black markings of the female are not quite as extensive.

Characteristics and Behaviour   These forest Grouse when mature are very sedentary. This is especially so with cocks. Once a cock bird has occupied and established a territory he is very restricted in his movements according to studies in the United States by Dr Gillion and others. However, during the remainder of the year, especially in the spring, cocks advertise their presence by wing drumming, usually from a favourite tree stump or log. This display effectively spaces cock birds out over available territory. Persistent intruders will be chased off by a ground rush with the head held forward and mantle distended, while the wings are trailed stiffly.

Habitat   Either deciduous or mixed conifer and deciduous forests. This species prefers stands from thicket stage to climax. Preferred tree species are Birches and Aspens, while apparently open canopy forest and young regeneration tends to be less ideal, in some measure due to increased predation, especially from Raptors like the Goshawk.

RUFFED GROUSE *(Bonasa umbellus)*   **1.14**

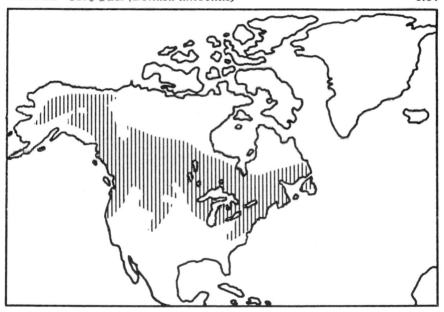

Food   The main food for this Grouse seems to be the buds and young shoots of Aspen, Alder, Birch and Hazel, with small proportions of Maple, Beech, etc. During the spring and early summer juveniles eat a lot of insectivourous and invertibrate material picked from low vegetation and from amongst the leaf litter.

Breeding   After advertising for a hen by stationary drumming from a favoured log or stump the cocks display around their hens, rushing in short spurts, fanning their tails and ruffs while hissing. They also in this display twist their plumage onto a sideways plane to expose to the hen the greatest part of the plumage while strutting. Not strictly monogamous.

Voice   Both cocks and hens use hissing, but the hen also has a distraction call while the young chicks which is a rather short, high pitched note. There is also an alarm call used by both sexes — *'peat-peat-peat'*.

Aviculture   So far as I know they are extremely rare in captivity outside Canada and the US where there is quite some success with this species by several aviculturalists who make much use of wire flooring in their facilities.

Sub-species   In Johnsgaard's book he names 11 sub-species including the nominate race, but this is confused further by the existence in all populations in varying proportions of two colour phases, the Grey and the Brown. I have reservations about the validity of all these and think four or five are more likely to be the case after revision.

Distribution   Extremely widely distributed throughout the Boreal and Temperate Forests of North America from the Atlantic to the Pacific.

Species: **GREATER PINNATED GROUSE**   **1.15**
                Tympanuchus cupido (Linnaeus)

Description Otherwise rather misleadingly known as the Greater Prairie Chicken, which they are not. Both sexes are similar in most respects. The major visual differences are eye wattles and nape crest or tuft in cocks. The latter either lies passively down the neck, or when erected forward is very prominent. During display a crimson neck sac is inflated causing the feathers to expose the bare area.

In general the colouration from a distance appears to be an evenly striped black and white barring throughout the entire body. On closer observation, however, the feather colouration is extremely beautiful, the white colouring being margined on either side with black, with between the black a lovely rust brown. From the rear, 10 prominent white under tail-covert feathers point upwards with the tail.

Characteristics and Behaviour   This is very much an open ground leking species much in the mould of the Black Grouse. Cocks are very faithful to their 'booming' grounds as the lek areas are known. After the breeding season flocks of considerable size can be seen in the autumn as these move between their roosting sites and feeding grounds, which are usually not separated by too great a distance, although in late winter foraging may force the birds into greater movement before returning to the breeding areas in early spring.

Habitat   Very much a bird of the Prairie land of the United States, and formerly Canada. Open grassland ranges and wheatfields are preferred habitat but land-use changes are partly responsible for an almost universal decline.

GREATER PINNATED GROUSE *(Tympanuchus cupido)* 1.15

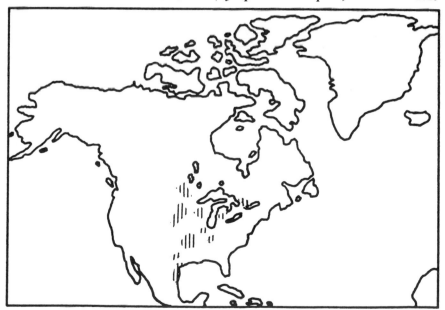

Food   Formerly buds and shoots of lower shrubs and trees on open or forest margins would have been an important element of the diet during winter and spring as with the Black Grouse today. Following colonization by Europeans this Grouse, while still eating all available types of seed including mast, has greatly supplemented its diet with cultivated cereals, both as a greenfood and as a seed source.

Voice   There appears to be a range of different calls, almost a repertoire, including *'pwoik-kwiee-kwarr-kwoo'*, and a cackle associated with the 'flutter jump' display. There is also, of course, the very significant 'booming' which is the greatest feature while leking.

Breeding   Having selected their mating partners Hens, after copulation at a lek, use long grasses, hayfields and rough ground as suitable sites to lay. The clutch of about a dozen eggs is incubated for 24 days and once hatched the family move off. Hens have the typical broken wing display pre-flight in chicks, but post-flight the entire group takes wing rapidly.

Aviculture   Kept for some time, mainly in the United States, and is quite suitable to normal captive Grouse management methods.

Sub-species
1. *Tympanuchus cupido cupido* (Heath Hen) — exterminated
2. *Tympanuchus cupido pinnatus* (Pinnated Grouse)
3. *Tympanuchus cupido attwateri* (Attawaters Pinnated Grouse)
4. *Tympanuchus cupido pallidinctus* (Lesser Pinnated Grouse)

Distribution   Central prairies of North America, greatly reduced in range now with Attwatters officially listed as endangered, this sub-species is found in Texas and the Gulf of Mexico and is very rare.

Species: LESSER PINNATED GROUSE   1.16
            Tympanuchus pallidicinctus
Description Somewhat smaller than the Greater Pinnated Grouse or Prairie Chicken and for a long time regarded as Clinal race or sub-species, but now several authorities feel the differences justifies a full specific status.

Although basically similar this species is obviously smaller and rather darker with alternate barring of brown and blackish brown. Instead of the yellowish skin of the sacs these are reddish while the eye wattles are noticeably larger than those of the Greater Pinnated Grouse.

Characteristics and Behaviour   In all respects the same as for the larger species.

Habitat   Extensive areas of 'steppe' like grassland and open scrubland of mainly Oak with Sand sage.

LESSER PINNATED GROUSE *(Tympanuchus pallidicinctus)*   **1.16**

Food   Seeds of Grasses, Sage and Acorns, buds and shoots of shrubs. Nowadays this is also supplemented by cultivated cereals.

Voice   Similar to the Greater Pinnated Grouse.

Breeding   As above.

Aviculture   Mainly kept by US aviculturalists and suitable for captive propagation using the usual methods.

Sub-species   *Tympanuchus pallidinctus attwateri.*
          Attwaters Pinnated Grouse.

Distribution   Southern United States with Attwaters sub-species found in Texas and the Gulf of Mexico. Attwaters is listed as endangered being now very rare.

Species: **SHARPTAILED GROUSE**   **1.17**
Tympanuchus phasianellus (Linneaus)

Description Very closely related to the Pinnated Grouse and similar
in quite a number of characteristics. Rather than having
the distinct barring in the feathers they give the appearance of being more speckled. The overall appearance
is a tan brown with white markings on the wings and
breast. Neck and back feathers are basically white with
brown margins. The tail is, however, quite different,
virtually triangular in shape and upward pointing, fawn
coloured and brown tipped. The ventral area is white,
grading to fawn on the belly where there is also brown
feather ticking.

Characteristics and Behaviour   Of the two extant species perhaps
the Sharptailed Grouse is the more primitive form. Apparently this
Grouse used to have a migrational shift in large parts of its distribution. Recent research does not suggest this now happens very
much, if at all. After breeding, Sharptails sometimes flock up, with
several families making up loose coveys during the autumn. Onset

SHARPTAILED GROUSE *(Tympanuchus phasianellus)*   **1.17**

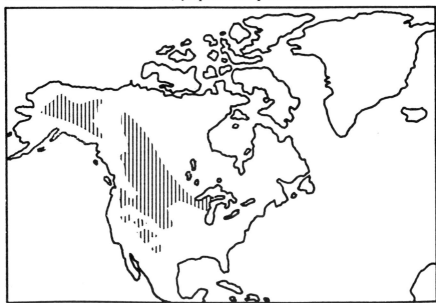

of winter leads to the break up of coveys as birds return to more restricted home ranges from the onset of the spring leking. The flutter jump display is apparently virtually the same as for the Pinnated Grouse, but while inflating the neck sack like that species the Sharptails do not 'boom' but rather call with a 'coo' tone.

Habitat   Although an open site species, Sharptailed Grouse are not nearly so restricted to specific habitats as their relatives are to Prairie type areas. While utilising such areas these Grouse also favour open forest up to 50% tree covered, but the ideal seems to be around 30% woodland cover.

Voice   In addition to the 'cooing' call referred to above other calls recorded include, for example: *'pow', 'lock-a-lock', 'cha', 'chilk'* and a *cork* popping noise which is not too unsuggestive of the Capercaillie and may indicate some sort of close evolutionary relationship.

Breeding   Nesting is usually in a secluded place with incubation of the dozen or so eggs for 24 days. After hatching the hen seeks suitable food for the chicks during their early weeks, particularly invertibrates, insects and greens.

Aviculture   So far as I know this Grouse has not been kept in aviculture outside Canada and the United States. I assume its maintenance and management is similar to that of the Pinnated Grouse.

Sub-species   Six sub-species including the nominate race are identified, and again validity of some of these seems doubtful. *Tympannchus phasianellus compestris*, The Prairie Sharptail, seems valid and is probably synonymous with *T.p. jamesi*, the Plains Sharptail. The Alaskan Sharptail is probably also valid. This is *T.p. caurus*, and represents an isolated population.

Distribution   Largely found in Canada and adjacent areas of the USA where it seems to be under pressure and declining in a number of areas.

Species: SAGE GROUSE   1.18
Centrocercus urophasianus (Bonaparte)
Description A quite remarkable Grouse with an outstanding leking display. Both sexes are basically similar in ground colour of blackish brown. The hen has lighter white chest and

flank feathers with both sexes having a black belly and
ventral area. The two remarkable differences occurring
in cock birds are their sharply pointed outer tail primaries which, during display, radiate outwards being
black brown in colour with white collar rather like a
Clydesdale Draught Horse which, when inflated, looks
like a white fox fur collar with black, delicate, soft crest
edge. On the back and wings of both sexes the muted
brown tones are finely marginated and flecked with
white.

Characteristics and Behaviour   Not   a   very   well   studied   Grouse
species at all, but what is apparent is that this species is a leking one.
They make great use of the Sagebush for cover, and for food and
shelter during the winter.

Because of habitat preferences there do seem to be altitudinal
migrations in severe weather. This apart, there do not seem to be
many other noticeable population movements either amongst cocks
or hens, although juveniles do seem to disperse widely.

SAGE GROUSE *(Centrocercus urophasianus)*   **1.18**

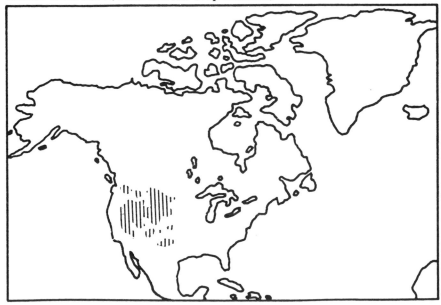

Habitat   Fairly species specific vegetationally to the Sagebrush, and, as with other similar species of dependent Grouse, there is a decline associated with reduction of Sagebrush habitat due to domestic livestock overgrazing. In southern parts of this Grouse's distribution the birds have also adapted to semi-desert scrubland.

Food   Greatly reliant on the evergreen Sagebrush, but other vegetation is also used.

Voice   When alarmed, birds have a repetitious *'wut-wut'*; Hens have an arrival call *'quk-quak-quak'*, and another call *'waa-uum-pooo'* with greater emphasis on the last segment.

Breeding   The hen actively solicits the cock after being stimulated by leking birds. She will then lay her clutch of 6–8 eggs in a secluded location where they are incubated for 26 days. Soon after hatching the hen with brood moves off for foraging.

Aviculture   Not kept in captivity outside North America and even there it is not a common species. Normal housing and management procedures presumably apply.

Sub-species   Apart from the nominate race which is the Eastern Sage Grouse there is one other — the Western Sage Grouse, *Centroscercus urophasianus phaios*.

Distribution   Although somewhat restricted compared with the past due to change of vegetation, some populations are quite unstable but locally improving. Found on either side of the Rocky Mountains in Montane habitats. Only just crossing into Canada, mainly into Alberta.

GROUSE HYBRIDS

Hybridisation is a fascinating subject when viewed as a means for establishing relationships, if any are present, or by its degree where hybrids exist between full species, and it is possible to learn a great deal in this way. In the natural state, for hybridisation to occur between species one must presume abnormal conditions to exist, for it is recorded quite rarely, relatively speaking.

Aviculturalists do produce hybrids, usually by accident, but so far as I am aware none have occurred in this way amongst the Grouse.

Deliberate crossing has, however, been done in Scotland by Dr Robert Moss, between Willow Grouse and Red Grouse. These hybrids are apparently fertile and this would indicate a close relationship. Dr Moss does express the view that these two birds are no more than races of the same species, Willow Grouse, but in this I would disagree, as full species — for example of Eared Pheasants and many others — are fully fertile and back-breed to either parents. No one would suggest they were other than full species.

Natural hybridisation definitely occurs between Hen Capercaillie and Cock Black Grouse, at least in Scotland. What remains unclear is whether or not these hybrids are fertile. In North America various hybrids have been reported with varying credibility. Of these, Sharptailed Grouse × Prairie Chicken seems to be quite common. An attempt was made to back-cross a female with males of both species unsuccessfully, although this occurs extensively in Ontario. Willow Grouse × Ptarmigan is strongly suspected from several specimens collected in Canada. Willow Grouse × Spruce Grouse has been reported several times where their habitats and ranges overlap near Hudsons Bay. Blue × Spruce Grouse is reported in one case in 1955 from Idaho. Blue Grouse × Sharptailed Grouse has been recorded only once, in 1907, from British Columbia. Blue Grouse × Ringnecked Pheasant has also occurred on several occasions.

The Caucasian Pheasant is reputed to have crossed with Red Grouse in Scotland, but one must be very sceptical of this. However, I do believe crosses occur with Black Grouse which, on the basis of habitat, makes overlaps seem much more probable.

A lot remains to be learned about the relationships between the grouse species and one obvious area is chromosome counts for all species as a basis from which to draw proper conclusions. Blackbilled Capercaillie are known to produce hybrids with the Capercaillie and these hybrids appear to be fully fertile back-crossed either way.

Chapter 3.2

Tetraonidae II
(The Snowcocks)

Snowcocks are very little known or understood as a genera, or any of the five species. They presumably once had a far wider distribution after the last glaciation. What we now see are relict populations isolated within suitable habitats amongst high mountain ranges from Turkey through the Himalays to Mongolia. The possibility seems very strong that at some stage Snowcocks diverged from the ancestral Capercaillies.

The species described are:—

Altai Snowcock	*Tetrogallus altaicus*
Caspian Snowcock	*Tetrogallus caspius*
Caucasian Snowcock	*Tetrogallus caucasicus*
Himalayan Snowcock	*Tetrogallus himalayensis*
Tibetan Snowcock	*Tetrogallus tibetanus*

The status of all species and their distribution is very unclear but some hunting pressure obviously exists, although this may not constitute much of a threat to their existence. Habitat disturbance is fortunately minimal and within the foreseeable future some efforts may be made to establish their needs and protection. Very few of these birds have been kept in captivity and little is known of their management, but currently attempts are being made in England and the United States by one or two aviculturalists, so perhaps we may soon know more. Owing to the paucity of information about all five species they will be treated and described together.

Description   The general impression of all species is one of birds which are stockily built, the sexes being more or less similar with cryptically coloured plumage. All species have black primaries and secondaries which show a noticeable wing bar when birds are in flight. Overall impression of colour at a distance is of a somewhat grey bird with whitish face and cheeks, across and down which is either a dark grey or a black chin stripe on either side. On the chest and flanks are vertical fawn or russet strips with variable black edging. The bills are stout and coloured light or dark grey horn. The legs are all unfeathered and either yellow or flesh coloured with grey or black horn coloured nails.

Habitat   Very much an Alpine bird, living above the treeline and following the seasonal snowline. Favouring rocky scree and high meadows. By varying degrees all species frequent rhododendron scrub of varying density.

SNOWCOCKS *(Tetraogallus species)*   **2.1**

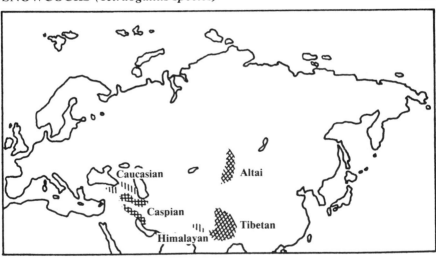

Food   Roots and bulbs are readily obtained by the birds digging with their large, stout bills. Insects and invertibrates are also eaten whenever available, as are grasses.

Breeding   Little is known, but these birds appear to be monogamous; clutch sizes are around 5–6 eggs. Replacement clutches may be possible.

Behaviour   In flight the Snowcocks are very fast with rapid wing beats interspersed with gliding. Sometimes when flushed birds will run rapidly, taking advantage of all available cover, especially when flushed uphill.

Aviculture   Very little is known but one can safely suggest that procedures and accommodation suitable for the Ptarmigan species of Grouse will be worth following.

Sub-species   So far as is known there are no sub-species, but it may well be that if the taxonomy of all the currently recognised species were investigated some of these may not be valid as full species.

Golden Pheasant

Chapter 3.3
Tetraonidae III
(The Pheasant Grouse)

There are only two species in the single genus and they appear to be a taxonomic 'mystery'. Perhaps not so much of a mystery as an oddity falling as they appear to do between the Grouse and Pheasants.

The species are:—

3.1 **Verreaux's Pheasant Grouse or Monal Partridge**
Tetraophasis obscurus

3.2 **Szechenyi's Pheasant Grouse or Monal Partridge**
Tetraophasis szechenyii

Very little indeed is known of these two species status in the wild and in all probability their full distribution is also not known. Because so little is known I propose treating them together and hope that in the foreseeable future more information can be obtained.

Description Both sexes are alike, and general colouration of both species is brown with greyish underparts.

Verreaux's has black barring on the back with black spotting and ticking on grey underparts. The chin, throat, and neck front, is a dark chestnut with mandible and unfeathered legs a blackish grey.

Szechenyi's is a somewhat large bird at 64 cm, as against Verreaux's at 48 cm. Again both sexes are similar in appearance.

The head has a black crown with dark brown on neck and back, grading to dark grey on the rump. Chin and throat is rusty coloured with the breast dark grey edging to a dirty grey on the abdomen and vertical areas. There is a muted brown or rust spotting and edging to feathers on the lower parts. Unfeathered legs and mandible are black.

Habitat Coniferous Forest and Rhodendron Scrub at high elevations.

PHEASANT GROUSE *(Tetraophasis obscurus)*   **3.1**
                                (Tetraophasis szechenyii)   **3.2**

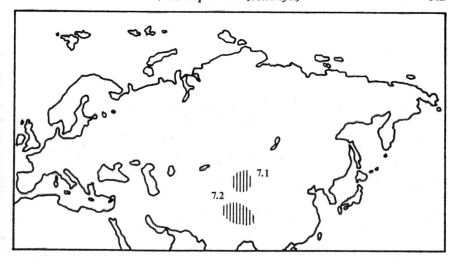

Breeding and Behaviour   Nothing yet known.

Sub-species   None.

Chapter 3.4

Phasianidae I
(The Pheasants)

In total this family has six genera, comprising 15 species as covered by this book. In total, however, there are 48 species, all of which are confined to Asia except two species, one of which also naturally occurs in Europe, the other in Africa. This Eurasian species has been naturalised in other parts of the world however, most notably in North America where it is also extensively hunted as elsewhere in its natural range.

The species described are:—

4.1	**Amherst Pheasant**	4.9	**Reeves Pheasant**
4.2	**Golden Pheasant**	4.10	**Mikado Pheasant**
4.3	**White Eared Pheasant**	4.11	**Elliots Pheasant**
4.4	**Brown Eared Pheasant**	4.12	**Himalayan Monal**
4.5	**Blue Eared Pheasant**	4.13	**Chinese Monal**
4.6	**Caucasian Pheasant**	4.14	**Sclater's Monal**
4.7	**Green Pheasant**	4.15	**Koklass Pheasant**
4.8	**Copper Pheasant**		

Several species of Pheasant are either rare or endangered, partly because some were never very common at best, but mainly because their status in the wild has been put at risk through habitat destruction. Further contributary factors, although less important, are the relative ease of hunting now possible and the availability of better weapons with which to hunt. A substantial feature of most species of Pheasant is the very noticeable sexual dimorphism, turning the males by varying degrees into 'a many splendoured thing'.

This particular group of birds has aroused a substantial interest, particularly amongst aviculturalists, who apply considerable resources to the keeping and propagating of these species in captivity, thus contributing to the saving of at least two species from complete extermination.

In dealing with Pheasants descriptively I must confess to a great feeling of trepidation; so many better and more able people have covered these birds before. As they are objects of very great interest to a vast following, particularly amongst aviculturalists of passionate enthusiasm, I hope no-one feels I have erred too greatly.

For want of a better description the 'Game Pheasants', as they are referred to by some authors, very rarely are dealt with other than by a passing nod to their existence and a dismissal as being 'too common to need mentioning here'. This is doing them less justice. The birds I refer to, of course, are the *Phasianus colchicus* species in particular, of which there are about 31 sub-species and races with diverse behaviour, habitat preferences and substantial plumage variations which in other genera would often merit possible consideration of revised nomenclature, placing some as full species.

It is all too easy to fall into the trap of aspiring to the apparently exotic when all the while missing out on some of the most subtly splendid of all the Pheasant family, otherwise also known as 'True Pheasants'. Personally I would never deny the obvious beauty of the Golden or Reeves Pheasants, but they have very little subtlety when compared, for example, to the Caucasian Pheasant on the one hand and the large Mongolian Pheasant on the other. Perhaps someone will take up a thorough study of the *Phasianus* Pheasants, for they are the most successful genera in *Phasianidae*, only being approached by the geographical range of the *Cotornix* Quails.

Hopefully the reader will see the justification of the reasonably full consideration of the True Pheasants that commences this section of the book. These Pheasants are, after all, of great economic significance in many parts of their range, a range which now through Man's agency embraces the entire geographic area covered by this book.

Species: AMHERST PHEASANT   4.1
Chrysolophus amherstiae (Leadbeater)

Description One of only two species in this genus, the other being the Golden, both of which are known as Ruffed Pheasants for obvious reasons. The cock has a metalic green head, surmounted by a backwards pointing red crest; the ruff is white with individual feathers marginated in metalic blue. The throat and upper body is dark green with black edging to the feathers. The lower back is black followed by a wide band of gold fringed below by red. Tail feathers are white with black barring, while the breast and abdomen are white with some brown marking along the flanks. The facial skin is blue, mandibles dark green and legs dark greyish black. The overall appearance of the hen is a reddish brown above spotted and barred with black. Underneath the brown is lighter with darker brown barring.

Characteristics and Behavior   A very hardy species and in the author's experience delightful and easy to keep. Cocks kept together with hens in a group will fight, but in a bachelor flock are quite docile. The courtship display is the usual 'wing dance' but this is greatly enhanced when the cock rushes up to the hen and tosses his

AMHERST PHEASANT *(Chrysolophus amherstiae)*   **4.1**

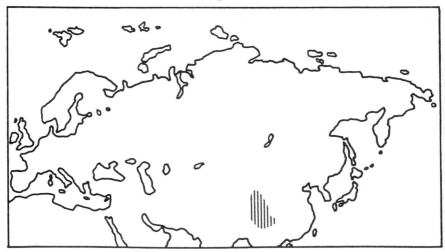

crest right over to one side, exposing most of the crest, which virtually obscures the head. The outer wing is tilted up exposing the back to great effect, while the tail is curled in the same arc as is taken around the hen. Autumnal flocking is recorded in the wild.

Habitat   A high altitude species (from about 2,000–4,000 metres) living on the ground in open, irregular forest of varying types including Bamboo thickets and shrub communities.

Food   Quite varied, inculding vegetation shoots and any invertibrates that opportunity offers.

Breeding   Fair numbers of eggs are laid in the wild (up to 12 and sometimes more). Replacement clutches are readily laid.

Aviculture   Easy to nest and can be induced to lay as many as 30 eggs. Hens make good mothers and several of them can be run with one cock. Because they like greenfood, a grassed aviary is ideal. Initial shyness is soon overcome and this species will share aviary-space if it is suitably large.

Sub-species   None, although impure specimens occur due to hybridisation with Golden Pheasants in the past.

Distribution   South-West China through to South-East Tibet and adjacent areas. Locally distributed in the United Kingdom.

Species: GOLDEN PHEASANT   4.2
                Chrysolophus pictus (Linnaeus)
Description The second of the two Ruffed Pheasant species. The cock birds are just as spectacular as the Amherst, with golden yellow from the rearward pointing crest, running down the head, ruff, back and rump. The ruff feathers, however, are marginated in metallic blue. The underparts are vivid crimson, while the wings have brown coverts mottled black with purple secondary feathers and dark brown primaries. The tail feathers are light brown and dappled with black. Legs and feet are dark yellow; the mandible is horn coloured.

Characteristics and Behaviour   Not very much is known about this species in the wild but it seems that cocks are so preoccupied with their individual vanity that not very much time can be spared for belligerent behaviour. There seems to be some indication of a leking type display with hens selecting from displaying cocks who defend an arena against other cocks and remain on site during the breeding season. This may also be the case with the Amherst. Autumnal flocking is recorded, some groups being quite numerous.

Habitat Rocky, high altitude scrub and undergrowth up to 2000 metres.

GOLDEN PHEASANT *(Chrysolophus pictus)*   4.2

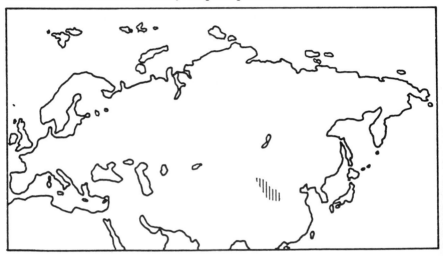

Food Sprouting vegetation, buds and invertibrates of all kinds.

Voice A piping, short whistle.

Breeding Clutch sizes are 7–10 eggs taking 22 days to incubate; the chicks are sturdy and hardy. The courtship involves the typical 'wing dance' exposing all of the golden back and side-held ruff when the cock circles the hen. A soft whistling note is also used during display.

Aviculture The Chinese kept these birds for many centuries and they are today the commonest Pheasant in captivity, easily outnumbering any other species. The Golden Pheasant is an ideal aviary bird best seen on turf with shrubbery. Most birds can become very tame and they make a beautiful sight anywhere.

Sub-species   None; however, there are two aviculturaly derived mutations, the Dark Golden *(C.p. mut. obscurus)* and the Yellow Golden *(C.p. mut. ineus)*.

Distribution   The Central Mountains of China. Locally introduced and free living in parts of the United Kingdom.

Species: **WHITE EARED PHEASANT**   **4.3**
Crossoptilon crossoptilon (Hodgson)

Description   Whilst recognised as the nominate species of the genus for the Eared Pheasants, neither the nominate race — the Szechuan White Eared — nor any of the other races in fact have any of the ear tufts found in the other two species making up this genus. Ignoring this anomaly all other characteristics are similar, including red facial skin, legs and feet. The tail is also typically long, large and gently curved. Overall plumage colour is white with tail feathers being greyish but having a metallic sheen. The wing primaries and to a lesser extent the secondaries, are grey.

Habitat   Similar to that of both Blue and Brown Eared species; high altitude Mountain birds on the margins of the upper Forests.

WHITE EARED PHEASANT *(Crossoptilon crossoptilon)*   **4.3**

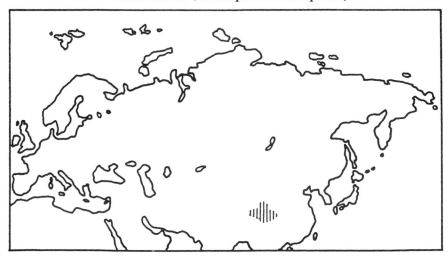

Food   Grubbing up roots with their strong mandibles and utilising any larvae and insects that offer themselves.

Breeding   Clutch sizes are slightly smaller (about 4–7 eggs), but they are in fact bigger than the other species. White Eared Pheasants are classed as endangered, but according to some sources they are not uncommon. Locally under threat due to changed land use. They are very rare in captivity, but rapidly increasing due to a great extent to the efforts of Jersey Zoo.

Aviculture   This species, like the others, needs large aviaries, and owing to its rarity should be given nothing but the best. Where possible maximum egg laying should be encouraged. The sub-species should be kept pure also, avoiding the temptation to out-cross inbred birds. Fresh imports of new blood lines will probably soon become necessary.

Sub-species   There are two:
1. *Crossoptilon crossoptilon drouyni* (Tibetan White Eared).
2. *Crossoptilon crossoptilon dolani* (Dolans White Eared)
The first of these two sub-species is entirely white in its plumage. The second is a pale grey and quite distinctive. None, or certainly very few, of Dolan's sub-species are in captivity at the moment.

Distribution   North Yunnan, Western & Central Szechuan in China.

Species: BROWN EARED PHEASANT   4.4
              Crossoptilon mantchuricum (Swinhoe)
Description A beautiful Pheasant and an endangered species. Apart from the black crown with the typical upswept white ear tufts, the general colour is brown in varying shades, but the rump and tail are spectacular examples of ornament with wispy white at the base and over much of the length, but ending in brown with a glossy purple. Again the facial skin, legs and feet are red, the mandibles being a fleshy tinged horn colour.

Characteristics and Behaviour   Very similar to the Blue Eared, and like the other species prefers to walk rather than fly. If kept in captivity and secure from predators they can be left free as park birds.

Habitat   Apparently more of a marginal forest species than the others, but otherwise similar.

BROWN EARED PHEASANT *(Crossoptilon mantchuricum)*   **4.4**

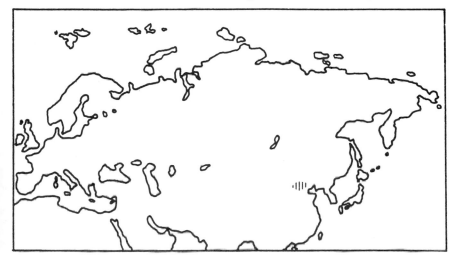

Food   Great diggers, using their bills to gain access to tubers, bulbs and plant roots, grubs and larvae. They also peck out shrub buds and new shoots from a variety of vegetation.

Breeding   Clutches of 5−8 eggs are incubated by the hen for 27 days; any clutches lost early in the incubation period may be replaced.

Aviculture   All captive birds descend from just a few birds imported in 1864. This has resulted obviously in too much close breeding which has created a loss of libido in many males. Efforts to remedy this with the importation of new blood and the use of artificial insemination by the World Pheasant Association will hopefully alleviate these difficulties. In view of the rariety of this species efforts to induce greater egg production are most important for future survival in aviculture and perhaps the wild too.

Distribution   The provinces of Chihli and Shansi in the higher mountains of North China.

Species: BLUE EARED PHEASANT   4.5
Crossoptilon auritum (Pallas)

Description Cock birds are generally slate brown overall but with
a blackish crown. Around the red facial skin are two
upward sweeping, ear-like feather tufts, each running
from the base of the lower mandible across the cheek
before pointing upwards above the crown. The tail
feathers are a deep blue overlaying white at the rump
tail base. Feet and legs are red with horn coloured
mandibles. Hens are similar but somewhat slighter in
build and having virtually no spurs.

Characteristics and Behaviour   All three species are most peaceable
with a strong pair bond and are definitely monogamous, being high
altitude species inhabiting open ground. There is an interesting
analogy with the *Lagopus* genus of Grouse from similar habitat
types. Aggression in males is only evident during the breeding season
when defending territory.

Habitat   Generally between the upper tree line and the snowfields
in fairly barren territory all of which is around the 3,000–4,000 metre
mark.

BLUE EARED PHEASANT *(Crossoptilon auritum)*   **4.5**

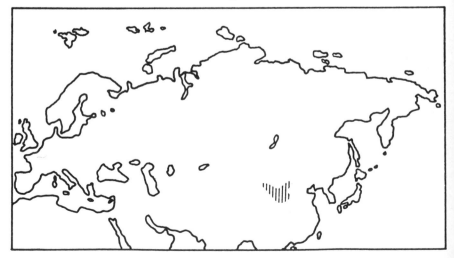

Food   Throughout most of the year largely vegetarian but survival of chicks is very dependent on the availability of insects and invertibrates. The stout bill is used effectively in digging roots, and they also take shoots and buds of low vegetation.

Breeding   The hen does the incubation for 26–28 days with the cock remaining nearby, again a feature of the *Lagopus* Grouse. Although clutch sizes are usually 6–8 eggs, replacement clutches are produced.

Aviculture   Because of their fondness for digging, large aviaries are advisable — if possible up to 25 metres^2, Double or treble clutching can be practiced. These birds are not much inclined to fly and they can be very tame.

Sub-species   None.

Distribution   The mountains of Northern China.

Species: **CAUCASIAN PHEASANT**   **4.6**
Phasianus colchicus (Linnaeus)

Description If would be fair to assume that most readers will be familiar with the general size of this bird, in terms of both cock and hen. In a general sense the cock bird has by far the most muted colouration of all the True Pheasants, which does not detract from his appearance. He has a very dark green head and neck with similarly coloured ear tufts behind the characteristic red facial skin and greenish yellow mandibles. The remainder of the neck is copper coloured, showing a reddish sheen of varying tone throughout the breast and back, all of which is feather margined in blackish green or purple. The abdomen and ventral areas tone from dark brown to a purple green. The wing coverts are fawn with brown markings, while the tail is a rufous red having pronounced black barring and tips. The unfeathered legs are greenish grey with a substantial spur frequently used in combat when circumstances arise.

As with all species of Pheasant in most genera the hen has very effective cryptic colouration, the base colour being light to dark fawn on the body with dark brown

CAUCASIAN PHEASANT *(Phasianus colchicus)*

4.6

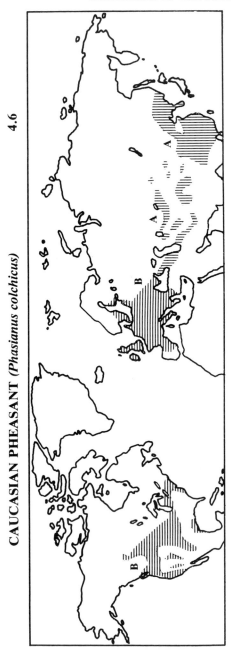

A. Introduced range
B. Natural distribution

feather marking. The neck and head tend to be a more rufous colour with light fawn around the eye region. The tail, while not as long as that of the cock, is also darkly barred but in a different way, having a brown band edged by a black line on the top and bottom of each barring. The Hen is slightly smaller.

Characteristics and Behaviour   Both sexes have a rapid flight and rate of climb with a sudden burst of audibly whirring wings, but it makes long glides with or without another short burst before landing, almost always on the ground. Both sexes will frequently run very fast before taking flight if ground conditions permit, as in cultivated fields and grasslands. Very little teritorial behaviour is seen in the male between the summer moult and spring, but occasionally a male may use his characteristic call in the autumn. Birds of all sexes operate independently throughout most of the year. Young poults grow rapidly and soon disperse, possibly as a defence against avian preditors. Roosting is invariably among the branches of the taller shrubs or on lower tree branches; in marginal habitat occasional ground roosting in a couch amongst undergrowth is recorded.

Habitat   The natural habitat for this group is originally open grass-land, steppes, lowland meadows and shrubby reedbeds. Nowadays, with most land under cultivation, these Pheasants have adapted very well everywhere and it is reasonable to assume that large scale cereal crop production has increased the numbers of birds throughout the true Pheasant's modern distribution. Currently considerable efforts are being made to artificially increase suitably attractive habitats and captive rearing in numbers deliberately for game shooting. The numbers of birds raised in this way for this purpose must amount to several million each year, and these birds are not wasted when shot, since they are eaten. As a consequence of this the Game Pheasant is a very important bird, providing much employment rurally from those who rear and manage sporting areas right across the board to many people in urban areas providing a whole range of products including incubators, proprietary feeds, utensils, rearing houses and pens, etc. The easily forgotten extra dimension is that the successful captive breeding, rearing and preservation of endangered species is largely based on the technology and expertise developed for rearing the 'True or Game' Pheasants.

Food   A great deal of time is spent by birds wandering through vegetation whilst feeding. Dependent on the season, their diet is varied and opportunist, utilizing grass shoots and seeds, insects and invertibrates of all kinds. In areas of cultivation they make considerable use of fallen grain after the harvest, and will also plunder fruit and vegetable gardens when reasonably secure opportunities arise. In extreme winter weather artificial feeding is often used to avoid significant population decreases.

Voice   A distinctive and fairly familiar call to most people. The cock bird has a display call in the breeding season rather like *'kur kuk'*. Both sexes have an alarm call usually made immediately on the wing: *'kuttuk kuttuk'*, sometimes longer and tailing off in mid phrase. Hen birds quietly talk away to their brood as a means of keeping the family together, and the chicks and poults use a repetitive piping call for the same reason.

Display   During the display or territorial call of the cock bird there is just immediately before and after a rapid wing beat which is quite audible. This is incorporated in a small vertical jump and is, when used by certain Grouse species, called the flutter jump. This display takes place within the cock's territory but not usually in the same place, although some general areas seem to be preferred. The purpose of this display is partly to advertise territorial claims in defiance of other cocks and also to attract the attention of the Hens.

Having brought in one or more hens to his territory the cock bird proceeds to court and display in the characteristic manner, with the wing held down on the hen's side, angling the body to the side and lower, while circling her, hissing and vibrating the wing primaries. This display or body language is also evident amongst domestic fowls.

Breeding   In the wild clutches of around 10−15 are usual but nests containing more are often found — sometimes due to two hens laying in the same scrape. The buff coloured eggs are incubated solely by the hen for 23 days, and replacement clutches are quite common.

Aviculture   More often than not reared for shooting, this species is easily bred and reared either on a wing-clipped flock system or in aviaries with one cock to 2−3 hens. I had one hen which laid 96 eggs in her second year and 41 in the first. This was a bit unusual, but by removing eggs as they are laid 20−30 eggs is not uncommon. Where they are kept in aviaries it is advisable to either pinion or wing-clip both sexes. The hens need cover for nesting, either with shrubbery or conifer branches strategically piled.

It is very difficult to keep this species with most other birds. I have watched one of my cock birds kill Finches by kicking them in mid air. Similarly Partridges, both Grey and Red Legged, are unsuitable, but Doves seem to be ignored. Newly hatched chicks can be sexed by examining the area immediately below the eye. Gentle inspection should reveal a wattle in young Cocks.

Sub-species   If all sub-species are accepted (and, as stated before, there are over 30), these fall into certain 'type' categories as follows:

1. **Black Necked Pheasants —**
    Phasianus colchicus colchicus (Southern Caucasian)
    Phasianus colchicus septentrionalis (Northern Caucasian)
    Phasianus colchicus talischensis (Talisch)
    Phasianus colchicus persicus (Persian)

2. **White Winged Pheasants —**
    Phasianus colchicus principalis (Prince of Wales)
    Phasianus colchicus zarudnyi (Zarudny's)
    Phasianus colchicus chrysomelas (Khivan)
    Phasianus colchicus bianchii (Bianchis)
    Phasianus colchicus shawii (Yarkhand)
    Phasianus colchicus zerafchanicus (Zerafshan)

3. **Mongolian Pheasants —**
    Phasianus colchicus turkestanicus (Syra Dara)
    Phasianus colchicus bergii (Aral)
    Phasianus colchicus mongolicus (Kivghiz)

4. **Tarion Pheasant —**
    Phasianus colchicus tarimensis (Tarim)

5. **Grey Rumped Pheasants —**
    Phasianus colchicus vlangalii
    Phasianus colchicus strauchii
    Phasianus colchicus sohokotensis
    Phasianus colchicus slaschanicus
    Phasianus colchicus seuhschanensis
    Phasianus colchicus elegans
    Phasianus colchicus rothschildi
    Phasianus colchicus decollatus
    Phasianus colchicus kiangsuensis

Phasianus colchicus torquatus (Chinese Ring Necked)
Phasianus colchicus takatsukasae
Phasianus colchicus formosanus
Phasianus colchicus karpowi
Phasianus colchicus pallasi
Phasianus colchicus hagenbecki
Phasianus colchicus satschouensis
Phasianus colchicus edzinensis

In addition, two colour phases have developed, probably from the Chinese Ring Necked Pheasant, the Melanistic Pheasant *(P.c. tenebrosus)*, and the Bohemian Pheasant *(P.c. flavia)*, both of which are extraordinarily beautiful. A point worth noting is that throughout this species range the general colouration varies from the darkest in the west to the lightest in the east. It was, in fact, the nominate race which the Romans are credited with introducing to Western Europe, including the British Isles. Of all the claimed sub-species only about a quarter have been brought to Europe and bred.

Chicks are relatively easily reared under domestic poultry, or hatched in incubators then reared under heated brooders, but they do need to be heat-trained initially. Young birds quickly panic if startled. They fly at a very early age and initially, if care is not exercised, cramped quarters lead to feather pecking and bullying.

Propietary chick crumbs and rearing pellets are widely available but moveable pens on grass are very useful, allowing the chicks access to insects, greenfood and exercise. Prior to egg laying, birds which are required to lay reasonable numbers of eggs should be fed on a layer's pellet. In aviaries roosting perches are utilized by some birds; others crouch under vegetation. It is, however, advisable to provide protection from prevailing winds in the winter and covered areas are helpful during rain or snowfall. If fed throughout the year, an aviary 12 metre^2 containing a trio of birds should maintain its grass cover. Liming once a year is advisable. Not infrequently intensive breeding has produced and still does produce hermaphrodite birds whose plumage is halfway between that of the normal Cock and Hen.

Distribution   Due to Man's agency this bird is now found throughout the temperate regions of the world, but its original distribution ranged from Eastern Europe to Siberia, and in all probability it is the least threatened Pheasant, owing to its economic significance.

Species: **GREEN PHEASANT**   **4.7**
            Phasianus versicolour (Vierllot)

Description A very beautiful Pheasant which has evolved solely in
Japan. Overall colouration is green and rather metallic.
The mantle is marked with black and buff, the neck is
deep purple, and the tail is a lighter green marked by
black bars with a purple edge. The wing covers are light
grey and the legs dark grey. The facial wattle is bright
red. The hen is a dark, muted green grading to black
with overall tan feather markings most heavily patterned
on the inside. For a hen Pheasant the female of this
species is very attractive in her own right.

Characteristics and Behaviour   Reputedly rather wild, yet often seen
in similar circumstances to the Caucasian Pheasant in cultivated
areas. Not a great deal is known of this bird in the West. Although
first imported in the mid-19th century there are very few pure bred
birds left. One can assume that in behaviour this species is much like
its Caucasian relative with whom it will freely hybridize.

Habitat   Mainly coastal plains and footpaths in cultivated areas
and broken forest sites along rivers and valleys.

GREEN PHEASANT *(Phasianus versicolour)*   **4.7**

Food   Very similar to the Caucasian Pheasant in almost all respects.

Voice   Again not very different at all from the Caucasian Pheasant.

Display   There is little reference to this literature on the subject, but while I have no experience of this bird myself I understand it is virtually identical to that of its close relatives.

Breeding   Clutch size is about 8−12 eggs, sometimes a few more. These eggs are similar to those of the Caucasian but a little smaller.

Aviculture   There are not many in captivity which seems a shame, and as they are not so prolific there has been an unfortunate tendency to cross this bird with the Caucasian using the spare Cocks. Aviary conditions similar to the Caucasian will produce satisfactory results and the birds are quite hardy but rather nervous, which may be one reason for low numbers due to lack of interest. It would be nice to see a stock of pure bred birds firmly established at some time.

Sub-species   There are three generally recognised sub-species:
1. *Phasianus versicolor versicolor* (Southern Green)
2. *Phasianus versicolor tanensis* (Pacific Green)
3. *Phasianus versicolor rubustipes* (Northern Green)

Distribution   Excepting Yezo, universally throughout Japan.

Species: COPPER PHEASANT   4.8
            Syrmaticus syrmaticus (Temminck)

Description The head, neck, chest and abdomen are a beautiful
            golden brown with feather bases marked black, while
            the outer edges are a reddish gold. On the back and
            rump the edges of the feathers change to white. The long
            tail feathers are broadly banded alternately black and
            chestnut. The legs are grey, while the facial wattles are
            red; the mandibles are rather yellowish. In the hen
            colouring is much plainer as can be imagined, with the
            head and neck being mottled brown. The bulk of the
            body is a mottled black and brown, with lighter grey
            tones towards the rump and grey on the chest grading to
            a lighter shade towards the vent. The tail has the same
            broad barring as that of the cock, but grey replaces the

black with lighter brown alternate bars. In her own way
the hen Copper Pheasant is a rather striking bird and
most attractive.

Characteristics and Behaviour Cock birds are very pugnacious,
tackling all comers, specialising in cocks of their own species, and
quite prepared to indulge in wife beating. The hens give a good
account of themselves and if in the mood will readily make serious
attempts to fight amongst themselves.

Habitat Preferably high forest clad hills and mountains but during
severe weather a minor altitudinal migration is forced on residents
of territories higher up.

COPPER PHEASANT *(Syrmaticus soemmerringi)*   **4.8**

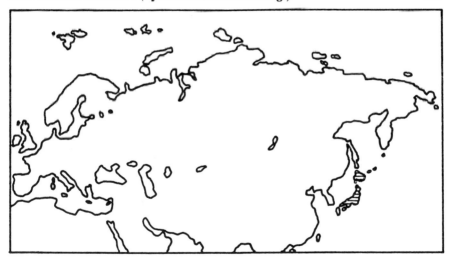

Food This species seems to need a higher protein diet than many
Pheasants, especially for the chicks which initially rely heavily on
insectivorous food. This is a fairly standard requirement for all
typical forest dwelling Gallinaceous birds, as with Capercaillie and
Black Grouse for example.

Breeding In the wild the hens must operate on a 'hit and run'
system in order to breed, but they survive to observe the results.
Eggs are usually laid from April onwards with second replacement
clutches as late as July. Incubation of the 6–12 eggs takes 24–25

days. The nest is a bare scrape amongst the leaf litter, usually under brushwood or the shrub layer.

Aviculture   This species of Pheasant is not very numerous in captivity outside Japan, where they are also reared for shooting, much as the Caucasian Pheasant is in the West. Because of behaviour problems the Japanese, who are very adept at using artificial insemination, rely on this technique to a great extent. The small scale aviculturist can, with certain precautions, keep this species in a number of ways including isolating the Hens from the Cocks outside the breeding season and wing-clip the Cock during the breeding season when they have to be together. Other suggestions include well concealed hideaways within the flight, especially around the perimeter of the cock's effective territory. Again, pop holes between adjacent flights, as used with Capercaillie, might be tried — large enough for the hen but small enough to discourage the cock, to a certain extent at least. Until very recently few Copper Pheasants were available in the West, but under the auspices of the World Pheasant Association a number of specimens of all sub-species are located in the United Kingdom as a result of importation of eggs from a Japanese breeder.

Sub-species   There are five named sub-species, but where ranges overlap a certain amount of intergrading occurs.
1.   *Syrmaticus soemmerringi soemmeringi* (Soemmerings Copper)
2.   *Syrmaticus soemmerringi scintillans* (Scintilating Copper)
3.   *Syrmaticus soemmerringi ijimae* (Igimae Copper)
4.   *Syrmaticus soemmerringi subrufus*
5.   *Syrmaticus soemmerringi intermedius*

Distribution   Throughout Kiusin, Japan, but mainly in the Northern and Central Regions.

Species: REEVES PHEASANT   4.9
Syrmaticus reevesi (Gray)

Description Possibly the most spectacularly coloured of the Long-tailed Pheasants, this species really does have a long tail, over 150 metres long. The overall impression of colour is a rusty gold with individual feathers edged in black, the wing coverts being white edged with black. There are 20 tail feathers, the ground colour of which is white and they are barred in brown and black with the body colour marginating along each feather and all of the shorter feathers. The abdomen and ventral areas are largely black while the legs are a brownish grey. Upper neck and head are white but banded with black from the greenish bill back around the crown, leaving a white spot below the eye. The base of the lower neck is a black collar between the upper white and main yellow body colour. The hen is a very muted version of the cock and much smaller.

Characteristics and Behaviour   A well-mannered Pheasant compared to the Copper Pheasant, but rather a poseur in front of the ladies during the breeding season, parading back and forth before raising his tail and throwing his tail backwards in display. The cock birds can be agressive but usually not to their hens, fortunately.

Habitat   The bright plumage of the cocks would suggest this is a forest species and that is exactly what it is, living amongst forested terrain between 500–2000 metres with slight population movements downwards at higher elevations during extreme weather in winter.

REEVES PHEASANT *(Syrmaticus reevesi)*   **4.9**

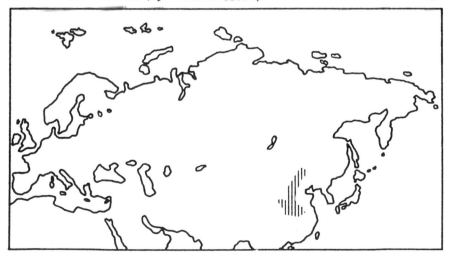

Food   Insectivorous to a great extent and also feeds on berries and fruits, with some seeds during autumn and winter.

Voice   None of the Longtailed Pheasants are very vocal at all. They do have a piercing whistle, most often heard in the breeding season.

Breeding   These Pheasants are prolific layers, clutch sizes varying between 7–14 eggs, but one or two replacement clutches are quite common. Incubation period is 25 days.

Aviculture   Because of the length of the tail, which often is damaged in smaller aviaries, a suitable size would be 20 sq.m. To avoid harassment of hens by the cock up to three hens can run successfully with the cock, but I do not know of any other bird which the Reeves will tolerate in an aviary. Both sexes are excellent fliers if they have to fly, so wing clipping in the first year is possibly a good safeguard. Chicks and young poults are noted for their quarrelsome behaviour amongst themselves and intolerance of other Pheasant young, so it would be well to monitor these birds a great deal. It is as well to remember that their being prolific and quarrelsome will put tremendous pressure on space for aviculturalists, and this should be borne in mind.

Sub-species   So far as I know none have been identified.

Distribution   Confined to the North and Central Mountains of China, but while not rare or endangered they are under some pressure due to intensive agriculture causing some de-forestation. Where conditions allow they retreat to bamboo thickets. Locally introduced in Scotland, Germany and France.

Species: MIKADO PHEASANT   4.10
                Syrmaticus mikado (Grant)

Description Completely black with a purplish sheen on the head and neck, while elsewhere the features are marginated with metallic blue. The facial wattle is bright red, the mandibles being mainly blackish, while the legs are grey. The tail, which is fairly long, has strong white banding along its entire length. Hens are smaller, generally black with areas of dark brown. Some white dashes run along the back and rump. The frontal area grades from whitish toning through to grey towards the belly.

Characteristics and Behaviour   Unlike most other members of this genus the Mikado Pheasant does not appear to be anything like as belligerent and, while numbers in captivity are small, little is recorded of their behaviour here or in the wild.

Habitat   Like most other species of Longtailed Pheasant, Mikados are mountain and forest birds at quite high altitudes of 2,000–3,000 metres on the island of Taiwan, the rule being, it seems, that the further south in group distribution one goes the higher the altitude needed by the representative species to satisfy its habitat preferences.

MIKADO PHEASANT *(Syrmaticus mikado)*   **4.10**

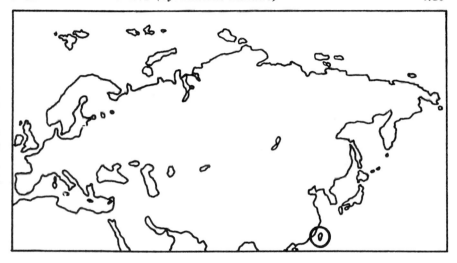

Food   In the wild reportedly largely feeding on vegetation, but it would be most surprising if this was entirely so as it is a feature of the Longtailed Pheasant that, like other forest dwelling game birds, they utilise considerable amounts of insectivorous and invertibrate foods as a source of protein, especially in the spring and early summer. No doubt at other times they consume quantities of greenfood and wild fruits too.

Display   Not a very strong performer, although generally black this Pheasant is very attractive and may not have needed to develop a sophisticated repertoire other than the typical wing droop and rattle with an encircling parade around the hen.

Breeding   The unusually large eggs, by comparison with other similar species, take 27 days to incubate and vary from 5–10 per clutch. This is an endangered species and it is very fortunate that Mikado hens can be induced to lay 2−3 clutches numbering as many as 30 eggs in total.

Aviculture   It is very prudent to run 2−3 hens with each cock just in case of harassment. This is a species which with imagination can be displayed well in a carefully thought out landscaping exercise; an aviary about 20 meter^2 would be adequate. As with all species of this genus the Mikado is hardy throughout the Temperate Zone, and with suitable protection against wind in winter there need be no great problems.

Sub-species   None.

Distribution   Entirely restricted to central Taiwan, off the Chinese mainland.

Species: ELLIOTS PHEASANT   4.11
          Syrmaticus ellioti (Swinhoe)
Description Cocks have a brownish-grey crown grading to a blue-
           grey at the back; the sides of the neck are white with
           a black throat. The chest, back and wing covers are
           bronze with two white bars on the latter. Saddles are
           vermiculated with bronze and white. The underbody is
           mainly white with some chestnut round the margins.
           The hen is cryptically coloured in a much more muted
           form and noticeably smaller.

Characteristics and Behaviour   This is one of the endangered species of Pheasant but its sheer agressiveness does little to improve its prospects, especially in captivity. This aggression is heightened by the breeding season and unless carefully controlled will result in the death of the Hen(s).

Habitat   Another forest-mountain species, but not found very high up which means this species is very sedentary.

Food   Highly insectivorous.

Display   Fairly minimal; cocks are just thorough chauvinists!

Breeding   When hens survive the cocks contact they are really quite freely breeding; clutches have 6−8 eggs with more than one clutch under certain circumstances.

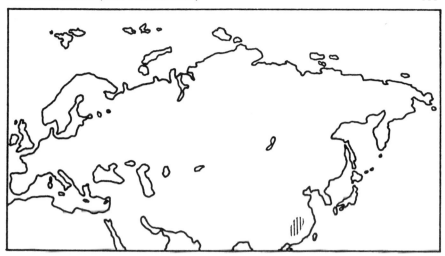

ELLIOTS PHEASANT *(Syrmaticus elliotl)*   **4.11**

Aviculture   It is important that care be taken with the breeding of this species due to its endangered status. A steady build up of numbers is needed. Double clutching should be encouraged as a means to this end, and particularly aggressive cocks ought to be segregated during the breeding season as much as is practicable.

Sub-species   None known.

Distribution   The provinces of Chekiang, Fokien and Anhwei in South Eastern China, under some pressure due to expanding agriculture and forest exploitation.

Species: **HIMALAYAN MONAL**   **4.12; 4.13; 4.14**
               Lophophorus impeyanus (Latham)
Description A very sturdy group of Pheasants, the only detailed description available of any species in this genus is of the Himalayan Monal or Impeyan Pheasant. It is not possible to describe either the Chinese or Sclater's Monal properly as they appear to be very rare in the wild. Even this is not precisely known, but they are regarded as officially endangered and not very likely

to be available to aviculturalists*. All the Monals are stockily built with large spurs on their relatively short legs. The upper mandible is unusual in that it overlies the bulk of the lower mandible and is strong and curved as befits a bird seeking food underground at certain times of the year, such as bulbs and roots in ground frequently stony and often frozen. The cock bird is generally black from the throat, and chest to the ventral area. The head is a light metallic green with a crown crest of a slightly darker green pointing backwards horizontally. The upper back is a golden tinged green while the overall wing colour is a purplish blue, slightly lighter on feather margins. The lower back is white with the tail feathers of a russet brown, but it is not a very long tail compared with many other pheasants.

Characteristics and Behaviour   Not a great deal of ornithological study or details are available on any of the species. The cocks are known to be aggressive, particularly in the breeding season. The hen incubates attended by the cock who does not however, brood the eggs. In the autumn the hens move with their broods to lower altitudes.

Habitat   A very high altitude, mountain dwelling genus about the tree line on open ground and sparse forest.

Food   As mentioned above great reliance is placed on roots and other vegetable material including fruit and seeds; also larvae and other insect materials.

Display   This genera does not have a very sophisticated display by all accounts.

Breeding   While the hen is incubating her clutch of 4−8 eggs for 28 days the male remains in the vicinity, as with other genera from similar habitats.

Aviculture   A large aviary is needed and as with all high altitude species it must be well drained. Because of the grubbing behaviour of the birds turf is unlikely to last long and a wire floor is likely to

*Since writing this *San Diego Zoo* have imported and bred from a pair of Chinese Monals.

A. Himalayan	4.12
B. Sclaters	4.13
C. Chinese	4.14

HIMALAYAN MONAL *(Lophophorus impeyanus)*   4.12; 4.13; 4.14

create behavioural problems with displacement activity in the form of feather picking.

Distribution   Not well defined at all, but on the southern limit of the area covered by this book, ranging from North Eastern Afhganistan along the Himalayas on both sides, including parts of Tibet and China.

Species: **KOKLASS PHEASANT**   **4.15**
           Pucrasia macrolopha (Lesson)

Description A very varied species not easy to describe as there are several races which differ considerably. Almost as if some of them were well down the road to a full specification. Cock birds have a horizontally protruding black crest which when walking is carried pointed towards the rump and tail. In both sexes the head is completely feathered. The general impression is of a light and dark grey bird with heavy black 'ticking' overall, front and neck. In some cases there is a yellowish collar. Tail feathers are dark and light brown while the back varies from mostly blackish brown through to chestnut. The

bill is a blackish horn colour with the unfeathered legs
a dark greyish blue. Hen birds are slightly smaller with
a more subdued colouring and have a shorter crest.

Characteristics and Behaviour   A high mountain species, used to
cold weather and not normally seen in groups larger than what might
be taken to be family parties. Monogamous birds, pairs remain
together throughout the year is typical for birds from high altitudes.
When courting, cock birds display by erecting the crest and puffing
out their body feathers. Birds of both sexes are very wary and take
flight quickly travelling fast. Roosting generally in trees at dusk.

Habitat   Usually found around the tree line, but moving up and
down according to weather conditions and season.

KOKLASS PHEASANT *(Pucrasia macrolopha)*   **4.15**

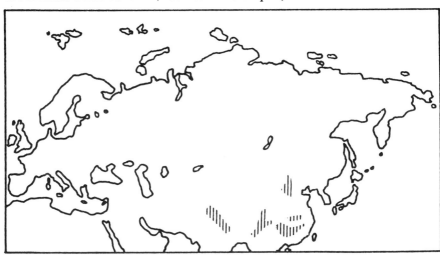

Food   Invertebrates and insects are much sought after but possibly
also young shoots and bulbs, hysomes and similar plant material.

Breeding   Nests are amongst clumps of dense vegetation and con-
tain around five to eight eggs which are buff coloured with dark
brown blotches and spots.

Aviculture   Very prone to illness in humid conditions and require
a varied and high protein diet. Not a very common pheasant in captivity owing to some difficulties experienced in certain climates.

Sub-species   Several, about nine or ten in fact from a very wide distribution.

Distribution   Found from the Afghanistan border with China and USSR in the west, through Kashmir and along the Himalayas to a mid-point in Nepal with a long break until the Chinese-Assam border, up to Mongolia in the North toward Formosa in the East.

PHEASANT HYBRIDS

Undoubtedly natural hyrbidization does occur among various species and genera. Some, but obviously not all, examples are known and recorded. In captivity considerable hyrbidization does occur amongst avicultural collections with varying degrees of fertility.

A record of some of these occurrences follows, but may well not be complete.

1. Caucasian × Black Grouse
2. Caucasian × Capercaillie
3. Caucasian × Domestic Fowl
4. Caucasian × Copper
5. Caucasian × Green
6. Caucasian × Cheer
7. Caucasian × Reeve's
8. Caucasian × Elliot's
9. Caucasian × Hume's
10. Caucasian × Golden
11. Caucasian × Amherst's
12. Reeve's × Elliot's
13. Reeve's × Amherst
14. Mikado × Elliot's
15. Copper × Golden
16. Golden × Reeve's
17. Golden × Green
18. Amherst × Green
19. Amherst × Monal
20. Amherst × Elliot
21. Amherst × Golden

No doubt there are several others occurring within the geographical region covered by this book. There are certainly numerous examples with other species outside its scope.

Apart from investigating species and generic relationships for scientific purposes there seems no valid reason for such activity in aviculture. In fact it is very negative and justifiably leaves aviculturalists open to criticisms of wasting valuable captive birds badly needed for propagating increased numbers to safeguard endangered species.

One example, however, of the benefits of hyrbidization is the saving from extinction of the Imperial Pheasant. While this species lives outside the area defined here, it is worth a comment. Delacour discovered this Pheasant in Indo-China and returned to his home in France with a pair in 1923. Owing to the collapse in numbers during the war, crossing was made with the only remaining cock and a Silver Pheasant hen at Antwerp Zoo. By careful selective breeding over several years the bird now in captivity is indistinguishable from the original, and this may be as well for as a result of many years of war in Indo-China it is easily conceivable that what was at any time a rare species may now in fact no longer exist in the wild.

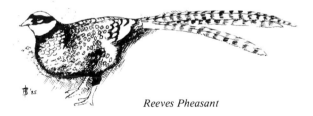

Reeves Pheasant

Chapter 3.5
Phasianidae II
(The Partridges and Francolins)

Here six genera with ten species are described. Within several of the genera there are more species than those listed but they occur outside the geographical scope of this book. All the genera and species have a natural Old World — Palearctic distribution. However, as a result of introductions by man for shooting purposes, at least three species have been established in the wild state in parts of the New World — Nearctic Region.

The species described here are:–

5.1	**See-see Partridge**	5.6	**Black Francolin**
5.2	**Sand Partridge**	5.7	**Common Partridge**
5.3	**Barbary Partridge**	5.8	**Daurian Partridge**
5.4	**Rock Partridge**	5.9	**Tibetan Partridge**
5.5	**Red Legged Partridge**	5.10	**Snow Partridge**

Species: SEE-SEE PARTRIDGE   5.1
Ammoperdix griseogularis

Description One of the smallest Partridges. Sexes are dimorphic
with the hens having excellent cryptic colouration, being
overall of a sandy brown colouration, darker on the
back with a slight rufous tinge to the tail. Cock birds are
generally more rufous with a black eyebrow stripe, white
below the eye with a grey cheek and upper throat. Outer
wing primaries are tipped black, while the flanks are
tinged grey, overlaid by horizontal reddish brown and
black stripes. The abdomen is fawn to white in colour.

Characteristics and Behaviour A monogamous species as are all
Partridges; cocks are typically aggressive to others during the breeding season — after which fledgling birds can be found in coveys often
of one or two families. Frequently seen running, or when in flight
usually travelling low and fast.

Habitat A species found in fairly arid areas with sparse vegetation,
seen frequently along such streams as exist and in the vicinity of
springs.

SEE-SEE PARTRIDGE *(Ammoperdix griseogularis)*   **5.1**

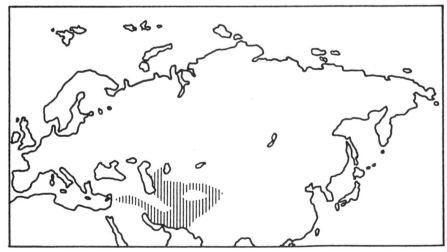

Food   Foraging widely, feeding on vegetation and rhizome roots, seeds in season, and any insects to come their way while searching amongst stony ground.

Breeding   I have no knowledge of clutch sizes and can find nothing in print on this. So far as I know around five eggs would be a likely clutch as this seems to be so for the related Sand Partridge. Hens are solely resposible for incubation.

Aviculture   Not apparently kept so far.

Sub-species   None.

Distribution   Eastwards from Turkey, the Mediterranean, Israel across to the Red Sea and Arabia, the Black Sea to Iran Westwards.

Species: SAND PARTRIDGE   5.2
            Ammoperdix heyi

Description Cock birds are generally tan brown throughout with lighter flanks barred horizontally by brown edged with black. Mandibles are reddish horn, while to the rear of the eye is a short but strong white eye stripe. Hens are tonally the same but the horizontal barring is generally light brown on fawn coloured flanks.

Characteristics and Behaviour   Monogamous, cocks are defensive of the core territory and see off bachelor cocks from anywhere near the likely eventual nest site. Very little is known of this species in the wild.

Habitat   Arid semi-desert to desert.

Food   Any vegetable growth available, buds, grasses, seeds and insects.

Breeding   Clutch sizes about 4–6 eggs and possibly double brooded during exceptionally favourable seasons. Cocks remain in the vicinity of the nesting hen.

Aviculture   As far as I know only Tel Aviv University has had any success with this species. Accommodation and management would be the same as for the Rock Partridge.

Sub-species   None.

SAND PARTRIDGE *(Ammoperdix heyi)*   **5.2**

Distribution From Southern Israel, down to Sinai and Western Arabia.

Species: **BARBARY PARTRIDGE**   **5.3**
            Alectoris barbara
Description Grey brown on the back, tail, wings and breast. The lower chest is reddish, the abdomen and flanks are pinkish white, the latter being vertically barred with alternate black and tan. The head and upper throat are slightly greyish white, being darker grey on the crown; the rear neck is reddish spotted with white. Mandibles and legs are bright red. Both sexes are similar.

Characteristics and Behaviour Not so heavily built as others in this family, but equally pugnacious. After the breeding season coveys merge for a time to form flocks, but these eventually break down later in the year partly due to avian predators.

Voice Two principal calls have been recorded, an alarm *'chukk-chukk'* and *'kakelik-kakelik'*.

Habitat Dry, stony and fairly arid areas with open, low scrub.

CAPERCAILLIE   *David Kent*
Cock displaying

BLACK GROUSE   *Bob Lambie*
Cocks lekking

PTARMIGAN
Winter plumage

Bob Lambie

WHITETAILED PTARMIGAN
Cock late spring

Ken Fink

RED GROUSE
Note winter plumage

Don MacCaskill

WILLOW GROUSE
Winter plumage

Tevvo Hietajärvi

SIBERIAN SPRUCE GROUSE
In Taiga forest

V. Veprintsev-Vireo

CANADIAN SPRUCE GROUSE
Preliminary display   *H. Aschenbrenner*

HAZEL GROUSE
Cock bird   *H. Aschenbrenner*

BLUE GROUSE
Cock displaying

Ken Fink

RUFFED GROUSE
Displaying cock

M. Godfrey/Vireo

GREATER PINNATED GROUSE
Displaying cock on lek

Ken Fink

LESSER PINNATED GROUSE
Displaying cock on lek

Ken Fink

SHARPTAILED GROUSE
Displaying cock on lek

Ken Fink

SAGE GROUSE
Displaying on lek

Ken Fink

AMHERST PHEASANT   *John Bayliss/WPA*

GOLDEN PHEASANT   *John Bayliss/WPA*

WHITE EARED PHEASANT   *John Bayliss/WPA*

BROWN EARED PHEASANT   *Ken Fink*

BLUE EARED PHEASANT *Ken Fink*

CAUCASIAN PHEASANT *Eric Hosking*

GREEN PHEASANT   *John Bayliss/WPA*

COPPER PHEASANT   *Ken Fink*

REEVES PHEASANT   *Eric Hosking*

MIKADO PHEASANT   *Eric Hosking*

ELLIOTS PHEASANT   *John Bayliss/WPA*

KOKLASS PHEASANT   *John Bayliss/WPA*

HIMALAYAN MONAL   *Eric and David Hosking*

WILD TURKEY   *Ken Fink*

SEE SEE PARTRIDGE *Ken Fink*

BLACK FRANCOLIN *John Bayliss/WPA*

RED LEGGED PARTRIDGE *Eric & David Hosking*

ROCK PARTRIDGE *Iain Brodie*

COMMON PARTRIDGE   *Game Conservancy*

BOBWHITE QUAIL   *J. Dunning/Vireo*

COMMON QUAIL   *Drawing: Iain Brodie*

CALIFORNIAN QUAIL

H. Cruickshank/Vireo

'GAMBLES QUAIL

H. Cruickshank/Vireo

MONTEZUMA QUAIL *Ken Fink*

MOUNTAIN QUAIL *R.J. Guiterrez/Vireo*

SCALED QUAIL *Ken Fink*

HIMALAYAN SNOWCOCK *John Bayliss/WPA*

CAPERCAILLIE NEST
At base of pine tree — Finland

Tevvo Hietajärvi

BLACK GROUSE HABITAT
Birch scrub — Scotland

Iain Brodie

WILLOW GROUSE HABITAT
Taiga Forest — Finland

Tevvo Hietajärvi

MONAL AND KOKLASS HABITAT
Pipar — Himalaya

Nick Picozzi

CAPERCAILLIE REARING PENS
Pop-holes for hens — Norway

E.R. Østmoe

BLACKGROUSE FEEDERS
Oil drums on tyres — Finland

Iain Brodie

PHEASANT REARING PENS
Brooder coops and rearing pens — Scotland

Iain Brodie

RED GROUSE NEST SITE
Located in rank heather (Calluna)

Iain Brodie

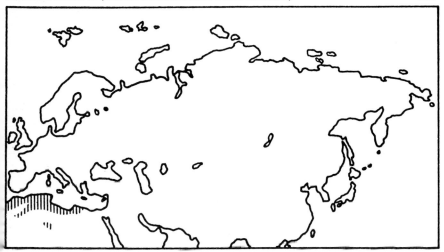

BARBARY PARTRIDGE *(Alectoris barbara)*   5.3

Food   Shoots of grass and other available vegetation, exposed roots, seed and insects according to availability.

Breeding   Hens brood their clutches averaging 10 eggs (sometimes more) for 24 days, but while they are busy they fill a second nest for the cock to brood too. The two clutches merge when hatched, making for large coveys.

Aviculture   Not a species kept by aviculturalists as yet.

Sub-species   None, although Sardinian birds seem larger.

Distribution   Largely outside the area of this book in North Africa, but also in Sardinia.

Species: **ROCK PARTRIDGE**   5.4
Alectoris graeca
Description   Greyish upper chest, rear of head and neck, back, wings and tail. There is a strong black line running from the eye over the ear, around and down across the throat. This sets off the white cheeks and upper throat. The abdomen is pinkish, grading to white on the flanks

where there are numerous black and brown marginated vertical stripes. Legs and mandibles are strongly red.

Characteristics and Behaviour   During the breeding season the cocks are rather belligerent; the hens also can be aggressive. Pairs may be fairly loyal all year round but this is not fully researched yet. Except during extremely dry periods, birds do not really travel very far from their own 'patch' until the broods break up in the New Year.

Voice   Various cals are known for this species — probably more than for any of the others in this family, which is not surprising with the very wide distribution of the Rock Partridge. These calls include *'chuk-chuk', 'pitchee', 'chertsivichi'* and *'kakuba-kakaba-kakaba'*.

Habitat   Fairly dry areas, sometimes quite arid and almost always rocky; usually hill terrain, often quite high up moving down to cultivated areas during the autumn and winter period.

ROCK PARTRIDGE *(Alectoris graeca)*   **5.4**

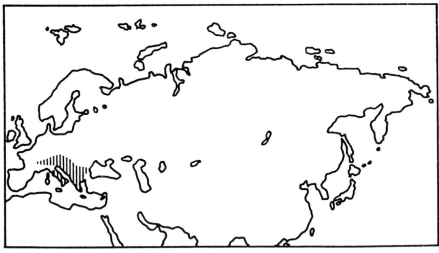

Food   Any available green tips either of grass, young cereals and herbs; seeds, small berries and exposed rootlets. Very fond of insectivorous food in the spring.

Breeding   Hens quite often lay two clutches not too far apart, brooding one while the cock broods the other, then amalgamating both into a small covey after a period of initial separation. As a rule this merging takes place when the chicks are flighted. Each nest contains 7–10 eggs and is incubated for 24 days.

Aviculture   Large numbers are reared for hunting purposes with best results under domestic fowls and incubators as these birds can be quite nervous and somewhat prone to desert nests if only slightly disturbed.

Sub-species   Several are recorded, perhaps the most familiar being the Chukar, *a.g. chukar*, mainly situated in the Middle East through Iran to Pakistan and India. Also *a.g. cypriotes* from Cyprus, and *a.g. pubescens* from Mongolia and Northern China.

Distribution   From Italy and the Balkans, across Asia as far as the Yangtse in China. This species has also been introduced successfully throughout the United States and parts of Canada.

Species: RED LEGGED PARTRIDGE   5.5
                    Alectoris rufa

Description Very similar to the Rock Partridge with greyish flanks
                    and a broken black throat and neck stripe, rather wider
                    in this species, breaking down into vertical lines. Both
                    sexes are similar with the cock slightly larger. The over-
                    all tone is rather browner than for the Rock Partridge.

Characteristics and Behaviour   Typical for the genus, and much as described for the Rock Partridge.

Voice   Diverse calls including *'chuka-chuka', 'chikk-chikk-chikka'* and *'tchakk-tchakk-tchakk'.*

Habitat   A lot less arid than the other species, frequently seen among cultivated fields, usually of cereals. Utilising fragmented cover of hedges, scrub and rough grasses.

Food   A lot of green vegetable material, especially sprouting cereal crops, grasses, herbs, insects and invertibrates; grain and grass seeds during autumn and winter.

Breeding   An intensively studied species in the United Kingdom, where they were introduced from France. Clutch sizes vary but range from 9–14. Incubation is 24 days and on hatching they leave the nest site fairly quickly.

RED LEGGED PARTRIDGE *(Alectoris rufa)*

5.5

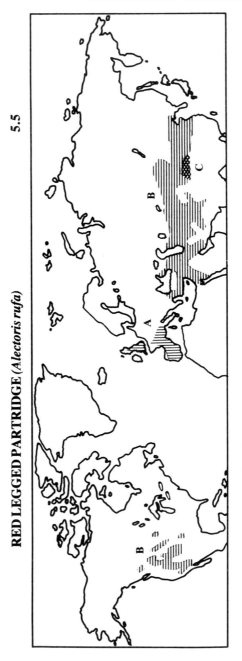

A. **Alectoris rufa rufa**
B. **Alectoris chukar**
C. **Alectoris graeca magna**

Aviculture   Large numbers of birds are reared artificially for shooting, especially in England and, to a restricted extent, in Scotland, owing to climate. Artificial incubation is safest using both domestic fowls and incubators.

Sub-species   None that I am aware of.

Distribution   Southern and Eastern England, France, Spain and Portugal.

Species: BLACK FRANCOLIN   5.6
            Francolinus francolinus

Description The cock Black Francolin is a very striking bird. A sexually dimorphic species, although the hen is not nearly so dowdy as in many other species. Overall the cock is black on the head, throat, chest, flanks, tail and tail rump area. The crown, back and wings are dark brown laced by tan feather margins. There is a neck collar of tan, as is the abdomen and lower ventral area. Over the flanks and shoulder are white horizontal feathers with a black central tick. The rump and tail are very finely lined with white crosswise, as are the upper legs. The lower legs are reddish tan but the mandibles are black. There is a horizontal white ear tuft extending from just below the eye.

Characteristics and Behaviour   In the wild these birds are shy and capable of very rapid flight, making them favourites for shooting. Loose coveys develop towards the end of the year. These break up with the effects of Falcons, other predators and the onset of a new season. In some areas dry and rainy seasons are also a significant factor on numbers using their respective habitats.

Habitat   Open Steppe type areas and cereal growing regions, also scrubby terrain.

Food   Very catholic in their tastes, taking whatever is available according to the seasons including seeds, insects, green shoots and other vegetation such as buds, etc.

Breeding   Known to produce more than one clutch; normally there are about 6–10 eggs which take 23 days to hatch. Hens incubate exclusively but not much more is known or available in print on this species, particularly on displays and calls.

Aviculture   Some limited numbers are kept and prove easy to breed and rear with double clutching readily possible. This species is reasonably frost hardy but is not too suited to excessively damp conditions. Insectivorous foods for chicks is essential.

BLACK FRANCOLIN *(Francolinus francolinus)*   5.6

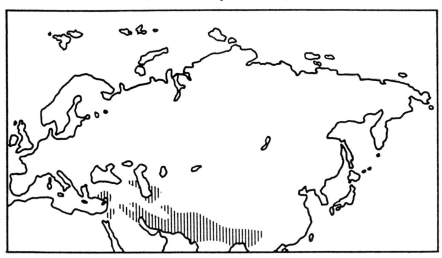

Sub-species   None.

Distribution   The Eastern Mediterranean, and Near East including Turkey, Israel and Iran.

Species: COMMON PARTRIDGE   5.7
              Perdix perdix
Description Sexes are basically very similar; hens, however, are
              slightly duller and the chest 'horseshoe' mark is smaller.
              Face markings are reddish brown, extending to below
              the chin. The crown, neck and upper breast are slate
              grey, so too are the flanks which are also vertically
              barred with light brown overlaid by side stripes of light
              grey. The abdomen and ventral areas are white, having

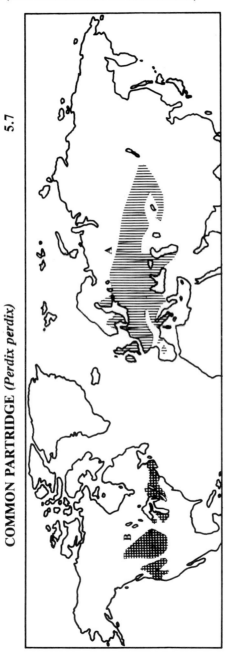

5.7

COMMON PARTRIDGE *(Perdix perdix)*

A. Natural distribution
B. Introduced range

an upturned brown 'horseshoe' marking. On the wings and back, plummage is tan with a horizontal striping of lighter colouration; some feathers have a dark brown margin.

Characteristics and Behaviour   Monogamous   birds   with   strong loyalties to each other, their young and their core territory. Ground hugging as much as possible, but when flushed these birds fly low and fast either as individuals or large coveys. After the breeding season coveys of family size or some merging gather in cultivated fields.

Voice   A well known flocking call *'cheer-cheer'* or *'cheer-it cheer-it'*. Rather grating and unlikely to be confused with any other birds.

Habitat   Closely   associated   with   Temperate   cereal   cultivation throughout the Paleartic Region and as a result of introduction is now found in similar areas in the Neartic. Regrettably severely in decline, largely due to the widescale use of pesticides and herbicides.

Food   Greenfoods, seeds, insectivorous and similar foods including visits to fields of sprouting cereal and then later returning after the harvest to clean up the fallen grain.

Breeding   Taking 26 days to hatch under the hen, the clutch of around ten eggs is usually found amongst long, rough vegetation and also out in the growing cereal crop. Cock birds stay close by the incubating hen, guarding her.

Aviculture   Easily bred in captivity although most aviculturists do not bother. Not prepared to share aviary space with other birds except perhaps Finches or Doves.

Sub-species   Eight races are cited in print but I doubt their validity.

Distribution   Eastwards from the British Isles to the Middle East, rare in Spain and now exterminated in Greece. Now also introduced to North America for shooting purposes.

NOTE: Two further species are to be found on the edge of this book's geographical region, both of the genus *Perdix*, the Daurian Partridge – *Perdix dauuricae*, and the Tibetan Partridge – *Perdix hodgsoniae*. Not much is known of either, but much of the foregoing must apply. In due course it may well prove to be that either or both birds are more properly sub-species of the Common or Grey Partridge.

Species: DAURIAN PARTRIDGE   5.8
Perdix dauricae (Pallas)

Description Like the Gray or Common Partridge *(Perdix perdix)* in many ways, however the main differences lie in the absence of dark throat markings in this species, a lighter breast and with a more irregular 'horseshoe' abdomen marking which in fact is blackish not rust brown. Females are almost identical with the previous species.

Characteristics and Behaviour Little is known about this species as compared with the extensive knowledge that exists about the Gray, but the little that is known suggests close similarities in almost every particular.

Habitat Open Steppes and unforested Hillsides.

DAURIAN PARTRIDGE *(Perdix dauricae)*   **5.8**

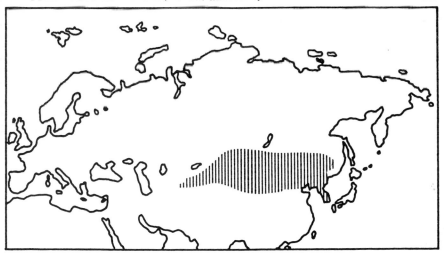

Food Insects, Invertebrates, seeds and grasses.

Breeding Identical to that for the Gray Partridge.

Aviculture So far none seem to be kept anywhere, but if it was the same principles as for the Gray Partridge, it would be appropriate.

Sub-species I have seen four mentioned but their validity is perhaps a bit doubtful.

Distribution   Russia, Mongolia, West and North China.

Species: TIBETAN PARTRIDGE   5.9
Perdix hodgsoniae (Hodgson)

Description There is less similarity with this species and the two preceding ones. The sexes are fairly similar with white eye stripes and cheeks separated by brown ear coverts. The back and rump tend to be a muddy grey with blackish feather ticking and barring. Chestnut underparts with bold black barring.

Characteristics and Behaviour   The muted colouration more suited to the high elevation rocky hillsides with all aspects of behaviour similar to the rest of this family and hardy with it as befits a mountain bird.

Habitat   Very ragged terrain with scrub.

TIBETAN PARTRIDGE *(Perdix hodgsoniae)*   5.9

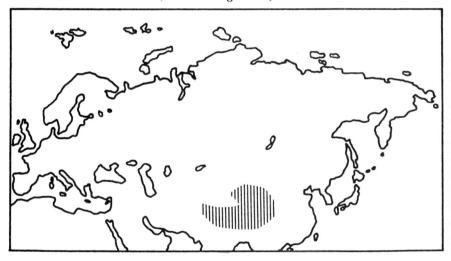

Food   Insect life, cereals and young vegetation.

Breeding   Little is known but typical of the family.

Aviculture   Not known.

Sub-species   None.

Distribution   Along the Tibetan border including Sikkim, Nepal and possibly Eastern Kashmir.

Species: **SNOW PARTRIDGE**   **5.10**
            Lerwa lerwa (Hodgson)

Description The only member of its genus, with close similarities to Perdix. This bird has a white chin, collar and eye stripe with a black cheek patch below a rust coloured ear covert, rust and black eyebrow marking and dull grey crown. Underparts are general off-white with black throat and chest barring changing to rust on the flanks. The back wings and upper tail have a grey under colour turning to buff with black and white vermiculated markings. A most attractive bird with both sexes similar and having grey mandibles and unfeathered legs.

Characteristics and Behaviour   Very little known or published, I would presume not very dissimilar from the 'Perdix' species.

Habitat   High elevation. Mountain grasslands with some shrubs.

SNOW PARTRIDGE *(Lerwa lerwa)*   **5.10**

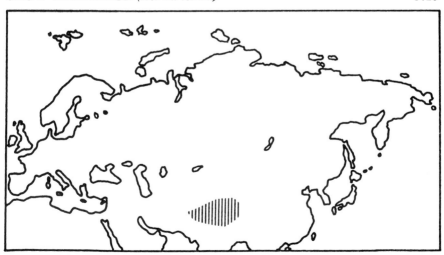

Food   Grasses, insects and berries in season.

Breeding   Not much known, eggs similar to 'Perdix' in number and colour.

Aviculture   Not known.

Sub-species   None.

Distribution   Afghan mountains, Himalaya, Tibet and Western China.

Rock Partridge

Chapter 3.6
Phasianidae III
(The Quail)

Overall the Quails are a diverse group of genera with an extensive distribution throughout the world. Many species adapt to extremes of climate ranging from arid desert to the humidity of tropical rain forests. The physical size of birds of this group is undoubtedly the smallest, but one of the species, the Common Quail, has the greatest natural distribution of any game bird, being found from the British Isles in the West to Japan in the East.

Obviously Quails have always been with us, but interest has recently taken a new turn with an increased study of many species in the wild and now amongst aviculturalists, with the World Pheasant Association even establishing a Quail Group for these specialist enthusiasts.

Described in this book are five genera, with seven species. The *Cotornix* super species are dealt with as a single species.

The species are:—

6.1 **Bobwhite Quail**   6.5 **Scaled Quail**
6.2 **Common Quail**   6.6 **Montezuma Quail**
6.3 **Californian Quail**   6.7 **Mountain Quail**
6.4 **Gambel's Quail**

None of the species of Quail have a Holarctic distribution although two Nearctic species, the Bobwhite Quail and the Californian Quail have been introduced to Western Europe and are acclimatised in several countries, including Germany, France and England. Attempts to do this in Scotland have failed on account of climate, and this seems a good thing because protection of indigenous species should be a priority, rather than indulging resources of all sorts in the establishment of alien species.

Regarding nomenclature of the New World Quails, there do appear to be some inconsistencies and confusion and I have dropped *Lophortyx* in preference to *Callipepla* for the crested Quails. To my mind they are all closely related and belong to one genus, and on that basis, for this book, I have used the oldest family *Callipepla*. No doubt I stand to be corrected, but in the absence of a better argument in the meantime I propose to ignore *Lophortyx*.

Species: **BOBWHITE QUAIL**   **6.1**
             Colinus virginianus (Linnaeus)

Description The sexes are strongly sexually dimorphic. The cocks
             vary quite a bit based on geographical location; several
             sub-species are described. The general description for
             the nominate race is used here; the crown, lower eye
             stripe and lower chin stripe are black tinged with brown,
             while the upper eye strip and upper chin are white. The
             chest, rump and flanks are vermiculated with chestnut
             and black, with white throughout. Wing feathers are
             individually grey and marginated with black edged by
             white, and some of the black is touched with brown.
             The back and tail are mainly grey with light flecking of
             black and brown. The outer tail feathers are slate grey.

Characteristics and Behaviour   Cocks are monogamous and pair
bonding is strong even to the extent that cocks will participate in nest
scraping. Pairs space themselves out by means of the cocks taking
territory and the success in this is based on social dominance established through display. Fighting in the breeding season can and does

BOBWHITE QUAIL *(Colinus virginianus)*   **6.1**

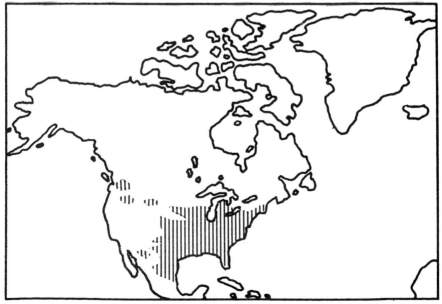

take place. In the autumn and winter birds flock in coveys and roost in small groups which are roughly circular, with their tails inward as a means of heat conservation, according to Johnsgaard.

Habitat   Open grassland and scrub where low seed bearing plant species are commonest. A rough guide to density in suitable habitat is about one pair per five acres or less.

Food   In the spring insect life apparently amounts to as much as 30%; various grasses, Maize, Corn, Soya and other cultivated plants. Acorns are also utilised in southern parts of the United States.

Display   In courtship the cocks approach the female with a frontal rush, head lowered, occasionally turning either side. Wings are fully extended and curved downwards but held high in a nearly vertical plane.

Breeding   Males exchange titbits and help in scraping the nest, which is lined with leaves. Clutches vary between 10–15 eggs which, when left unattended by the brooding hen, are covered with grasses. Incubation takes 23 days after egg laying at a rate of one egg per day.

Aviculture   One of the first North American species kept and very easily bred in large numbers. Hens can be induced to lay vast numbers of eggs, more than most people can cope with. The repeated whistle of the cock during daylight hours can be irritating to other than the dedicated.

Sub-species   Over 20 sub-species are quoted by the American Ornithologists Union and others, but they are not all listed here as I believe this number is ridiculous and based on normal variation by habitat extremes and latitudes. Few of these are genuine geographical variations and the others integrate so much that they cannot be defined properly. Below are some of the clearly defined sub-species:–

> *Colinus virginianus ridgwayi*   Masked Bobwhite. Endangered.
> *Colinus virginianus cubanensis*   Cuban Bobwhite.
> *Colinus virginianus pectoralis*   Black Breasted Bobwhite.
> *Colinus virginianus atriceps*   Black Headed Bobwhite.

Distribution   Central United States to the Atlantic Coast south to Florida, Cuba, Mexico south to the Gualamelan border, a little south of the area covered by this book. Introduced to the United Kingdom and West Germany.

Species: **COMMON QUAIL**   **6.2**
              Cotornix cotornix

Description While clearly sexually dimorphic, the cock bird is very
              cryptically coloured. The hen is a dark brown with only
              slight tan marking. Generally the cock is light brown
              with feathers marked with dark brown especially on the
              back, short tail and crown. The facial area and chest are
              light fawn. Along the flank are horizontal grey white
              barrings. There is a white collar at the front from ear
              to ear, above and below which is a dark, almost black,
              chin and throat.

Characteristics and Behaviour   A significantly migratory bird, and
the only species of *Galliformes* to have such substantial geographical
movement North to South during the winter. A solely monogamous
species. Coveys flock South in groups but return as a rule as pairs
or small parties at most. Very rarely seen but its presence is noticeable
from the cock's calling.

Habitat   Rough grass and farmland, particularly in cereal growing
areas in Europe.

Food   A seed eating species largely, but utilising small insects when
available.

COMMON QUAIL *(Cotornix cotornix)*   **6.2**

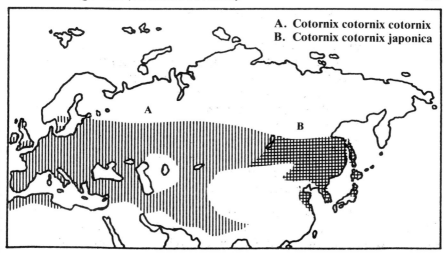

A. Cotornix cotornix cotornix
B. Cotornix cotornix japonica

Breeding   Not a great deal is known about this most widely spread game bird, which is quite surprising. Hens incubate their clutches without help from the cock who does however stay nearby during the 22 day incubation period. Populations show large fluctuations, but there is in Western Europe a definite trend downwards and this species is locally rare and endangered.

Aviculture   Very widely kept and bred, being very prolific and is even reared on game farms for food consumption. This intensive rearing led to mutation plumages, especially partial or total albinism. Once used to people this species is very confiding, to the extent of eating from the hand.

Sub-species   Only one in my opinion – *Cotornix cotornix japonica*, Japanese Quail. The main difference seems to be a fawn, rather white, chin stripe but there is a lot of individual variation.

Distribution   Throughout the Polearctic Region from the Atlantic to the Pacific, outside areas of Mediterranean climate, where they are sedentary, northern populations travelling up to 1000 miles (2000 kilometres).

Species: **CALIFORNIAN QUAIL**   **6.3**
            Callipepla californicus (Shaw)

Description The cock's crown, neck, back, wings and tail are blackish brown as is the facia area, chin and upper throat. There is on the crown what Johnsgard neatly described as a 'tear drop' crest which is also black. On the head, above the eye, is a white eyebrow stripe running down and across the throat, separating the brown speckled mantle and facial area from the slate grey of the upper throat and upper chest. Below this area, running down across the chest, belly and ventral region is a beautifully marked golden yellow to rust yellow stripe. Each feather is margined by a black-brown edging. Along the flanks is an irregular white feather striping. The Hen is a much duller version, but similar, only lacking the black throat.

Characteristics and Behaviour   Except during the breeding season this species is found in coveys based mainly on family groups to which odd birds or unsuccessful pairs attach themselves. At the onset of spring coveys break up to pairs before later taking up nest territories. An interesting feature of this species, which is also apparent amongst other temperate species, is the prominent vocalising of unpaired cocks from a song post which is usually a small knoll, boulder or other vantage point. This an indication often of a breeding pair nesting nearby, but it is not the breeding Cock.

Habitat Open grassland-shrub, chapparral and cultivated areas, varying from cool temperate to near desert.

CALIFORNIAN QUAIL *(Callipepla californicus)* 6.3

Food As with all Quail species the Californian Quail is according to season largely vegetarian or seed eating. However, while insects for protein for post hatching chicks are used to some extent they are not nearly so crucial as with larger Gallinaceous birds.

Voice Various calls, but the flocking call is easily remembered as *'chi-ca-gow'* and there is the *'ut-ut'* talking call amongst birds in a group.

Display Pair formation is a very subdued affair with little activity. There is a display by the cock, occasionally seen, involving a forward bow and rush.

Breeding   Occasionally cocks can be seen brooding, but this is mainly the function of the hen. Roughly 10–12 eggs is the normal clutch size with incubation taking about 22 days. Unusually in the wild unmated cocks are recorded as being permitted close to the newly hatched chicks, even helping with their care.

Aviculture   A very commonly kept species both in Europe and North America for some time. Prolific and easily kept, an ideal species for beginners.

Sub-species   Including the nominate race, the American Ornithological Union (AOU) indicates eight sub-species. To what extent these are all valid seems doubtful.

Distribution   North America, naturally from Baja, California up the West Coast to Oregon. Introduced further North and also in Canada, New Zealand and Europe in limited areas.

Species: GAMBELS QUAIL   6.4
Callipepla gambelii

Description Considerable similarities between this species and the Californian are evident, but they are undoubtedly separate species. The cock has the typical black 'tear drop' crest on a black to rufous head. The overall colouration is greyish with brown flanks. There is a black face with white eye and cheek stripes, as well as a black throat in cocks which is missing in the hen.

Characteristics and Behaviour   Throughout most of the year this Quail flocks in quite large coveys with as many as 30–40 birds, which presumably comprise several family parties and unpaired birds from the previous breeding season. Some aggression does occur between cock birds during the breeding season and those who have studied this species in the wild believe it to have a social significance rather more than territorial. Cocks pair off with hens over a period of time, pre-nesting as a rule, but they do have a display involving a circling of the hen repeatedly with distended tail and slightly fluffed up appearance, including wing droop.

Habitat   Primarily a species of arid regions with low rainfall and sparse vegetation.

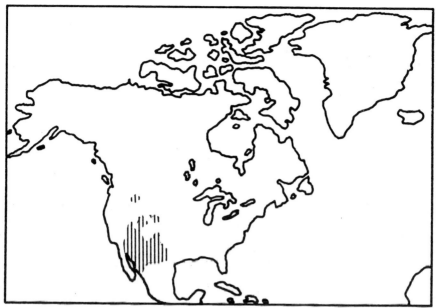

GAMBELS QUAIL *(Callipepla gambelii)* 6.4

Food   Largely dependent on plant seeds and some greenfood.

Breeding   The hen seems solely responsible for incubation over 23 days with the cock in attendance perched on a favoured bush. The cock will use a broken wing distraction display when danger threatens the sitting hen or brood. Double clutching is rare apparently, but when it happens the cock takes over care of the brood while the Hen incubates her second clutch.

Aviculture   Fairly well known in North America but relatively recently imported to Europe. Reasonably easy to keep but unsuited to very damp conditions. Numbers in the UK are increasing rapidly.

Sub-species   Inclusive of the nominate seven, but as far as can be seen differences (if any) are marginal.

Distribution   Southern Western United States and adjacent areas of Mexico.

Species: SCALED QUAIL   6.5
Callipepla squamata (Vigors)

Description This seems one of the nicest Quail from North America, having very subtle colouring of a blue grey on head, neck, throat and heavily barred breast and flank markings overlaying a white ground colour. The wing coverts and primaries are rust coloured with small white markings. Both sexes are quite similar and both have an erect crest on top of the crown. Even in the hand sexing the birds by plumage needs a little care.

Characteristics and Behaviour Large flocks are reported as being normal for this species, apparently in excess of 100 sometimes. A normally high, sedentary species of Quail. Aggression in cocks increases around March and coveys break down with the disposal of pairs to their chosen home ranges.

Habitat Fairly arid regions although less so at the northern end of their distribution.

SCALED QUAIL *(Callipepla squamata)*   **6.5**

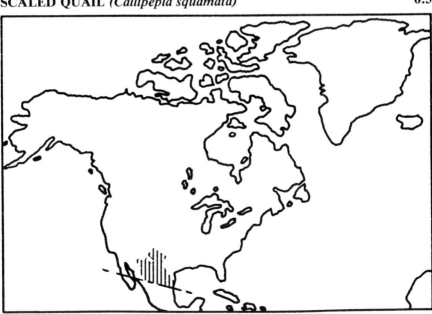

Food   As with the others very reliant on seeds of a wide range of grasses and other plants. Some greenfood is also eaten, with limited use made of insects.

Breeding   The nest scrape contains around 10–14 eggs which are almost entirely incubated by the Hen for 23 days. There is some evidence that on occasion cocks will finish-off brood rearing while a second clutch is laid but as a rule weather conditions often prevent even one clutch being produced in some very dry years.

Aviculture   There are reasonable numbers amongst aviculturalists in North America and as a result of recent importations to the United Kingdom in the late '70's there are increasing numbers of this attractive Quail.

Sub-species   The AOU names three including the nominate race. The only obvious one seems to be the Chestnut Breasted Scale Quail – *Callipepla squamata castanogastis*.

Distribution   South-Western United States and large areas of adjacent Mexico. Introductions have been made in parts of Washington and Nevada.

Species: MONTEZUMA QUAIL   6.6
Crytonyx montezumae (Vigors)

Description   The cock's head has a crown of deep brownish black with black throat, collar, cheek, ear and eye markings, all of which are streaked with white ground colour. The back is deep brown lined with tan markings while the chest, flanks and lower throat are dark brown, each feather being spotted white. The breast, abdomen and ventral area is plain dark brown. The mandibles are blackish grey with grey legs. The hen is cryptically marked, on the underside a grey brown striated and barred in black. The back, head and wings are vermiculated tan, brown and black. Indeed a well camouflaged lady.

Characteristics and Behaviour   Monogamous and seemingly pair bonded. Feeding peaks occur morning and evening. The cock and hen participate in nest formation and some observers record cocks incubating.

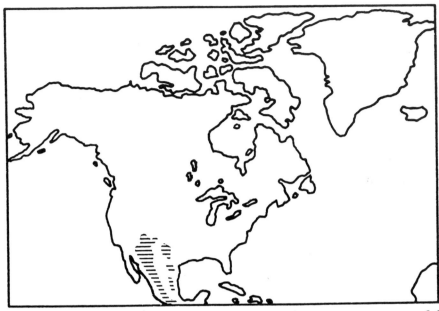

MONTEZUMA QUAIL *(Crytonyx montezumae)*   **6.6**

Habitat   Fairly dry regions in open Pine/Oak forests and grasslands.

Food   Great foragers amongst seed, bulbs and insects; roots and buds in season.

Breeding   Both sexes co-operate in nest construction, making a domed nest from available vegetation (leaves and grasses) with an entrance masked by other vegetation falling back into place on entering and leaving. Incubation takes 26 days. The clutch size varies from 6–14 eggs and each egg takes some 2–3 days to lay, so laying a full clutch takes quite some time. The cock takes part in rearing the young even to the extent of feigning wing injury.

Aviculture   Bred in captivity in the United States and only recently imported to Europe; there is very little experience of this species.

Sub-species   Four sub-species are named but only one seems relevant: *Cyrtonyx montezumae mearnsi* (Mearns Harlequin).

Note: The colloquial names vary, including Black Quail and Painted Quail but it is most often referred to as the Harlequin Quail. This name is the common name for another species previously named in the Palearctic Region.

Distribution   South Western United States down through Mexico.

Species: **MOUNTAIN QUAIL**   **6.7**
              Oreortyx pictus (Douglas)

Description   The sexes have fairly simple plumage. Unusually, both sexes have crests and two straight black feathers. The overall colouring is grey, dark on the back, wings and upper tail. The neck, head and chest are a slate grey, but the throat is chestnut with black edging separated by a white line above the grey body. Flank marking is chestnut but strikingly barred by black and white verticals.

Characteristics and Behaviour   This species makes altitudinal migrations based on the seasons. Daily movements are not great, with the birds walking in preference to flying, although if disturbed or alarmed they will take to the wing, rapidly wheeling uphill as a rule. This bird does not appear to have been intensively studied and not a great deal of detail is known, but it does flock in small groups after the breeding season.

MOUNTAIN QUAIL *(Oreortyx pictus)*   **6.7**

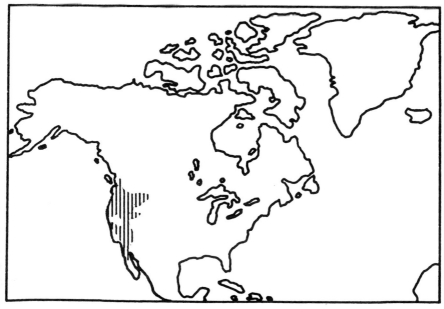

Habitat   Open scrubland, forest edges and around cultivated areas, the latter especially from the autumn onwards.

Food   Very varied, covering a range of fruits and seeds of trees both deciduous and coniferous. A fair amount of greenfood is consumed as well as rhizomes, roots, bulbs and insects, especially the latter in spring and early summer.

Breeding   No detailed records are available, but the cock has a very strong whistle clearly heard over several hundred metres. This call is often emitted from a log, rock or other prominent song post. Clutch sizes are around 7–10 eggs. While the cock is not recorded as incubating, he does stay nearby and in the main participates in chick care after a 28 day incubation period.

Aviculture   Not very common in captivity, most birds are found in the US, but some were imported to the UK at the start of the decade. Several clutches can be induced by removal, up to three dependant on latitude.

Sub-species   Including the nominate race five are recorded by the AOU:–

     1. *Oreortyx pictus pictus*   Sierra Mountain Quail.
     2. *Oreortyx pictus palmeri*   Coastal Mountain Quail.
     3. *Oreortyx pictus confinis*   San Pedro Mountain Quail.
     4. *Oreortyx pictus cremophila*   Desert Mountain Quail.
     5. *Oreortyx pictus russelli*   Pallid Mountain Quail.

Distribution   Along the West Coast of the United States from the Canadian border to the Mexican border. At one time possibly further East.

Californian Quail

QUAIL HYBRIDS

With all but one of the Temperate Region Quail species found in North America it is to that region we must look for hybridisation in nature. It is worth mentioning, however, that so far as I can ascertain no natural hybrids are recorded between the Common Quail – *Cotornix cortornix*, and any species from other genera. I am not aware of any aviculture hybridisation, and if it has occurred it must have been relatively recently. In the United States mainly, records of natural hybridisation, particularly of certain species, are not uncommon. Captive studies, particularly the very extensive ones carried out by Professor Johnsgaard of the University of Nebraska, reveal very interesting information both on which species produce hybrids and to what extent such hybrids are fertile.

The following information is largely a brief summary from Prof. Johnsgaard's published material to which he referred me. Dealing first with natural hybrids, these are as follows:–

1. Californian × Mountain
2. Californian × Gambels
3. Scaled × Bobwhite
4. Scaled × Gambels
5. Scaled × Californian
6. Bobwhite × Californian
7. Mountain × Californian

Captive hybridisation between various species of Quail has been undertaken, particularly by Professor Johnsgaard, who has also attempted, with varying degrees of success, first cross (F^1) pairings, second cross (F^2) pairings, and numerous backcross hybrid pairings. Some idea may be had of the resulting efforts these pairings produced showing the relationships that evolved by species. Professor Johnsgaard's work is very interesting indeed and leads to a better understanding of evolutionary origins of Quail in North and Central America (see Figure 3).

Chapter 3.7
Meleagrididae
(The Turkeys)

This is a family with two genera, each genus having only a single species. Within the area dealt with in this book only one of these is described, the other being the Ocellated Turkey from Central America which is very much a tropical species.

Species: **AMERICAN TURKEY**   **7.1**
Meleagris gallopavo gallopavo (Linnaeus)

Description Apart from almost hair-like, sparse feathers the head and neck of both adult sexes is bare with, in cocks, a fleshy caruncle on top of the head behind the base of the upper mandible and also a pair of flesh coloured wattles on the throat. The plumage has a metallic sheen of green copper and bronze, with the female being somewhat duller in appearance and only half the size; about 8 kg (17½ lbs) in males, and 4 kg (8–9 lbs) in females. Colouring of the breast is lighter and there is an unusual long tuft of bristles. Towards the abdomen and vent the colouring darkens to almost black. Tail feathers are marked with black banding over a brown colour, ending in black with white tips. The mandibles are horn coloured, while legs and feet are reddish. In the Cock there are large spurs. The nominate race identified by Linnaus is the South Mexican Turkey and it is this bird which is the ancestor of all the domestic Turkeys today, having been originally domesticated by the Indians living in that part of Mexico.

Characteristics and Behaviour   It would be no great stretch of the imagination to equate this New World species with the Capercaillie of the Old World. They are alike in more ways than not. A forest dwelling bird, a lot less specialised in tree species requirements than Capercaillie, the Turkey is, however, also a lek species but there are small migrations from the summer breeding grounds to the winter feeding grounds. The sexes flock separately and the birds all have a preference for roosting fairly well up in the trees. In flight they are much like Capercaillie; certainly not so fast but equally powerful owing to their weight.

Habitat   Very much less reliant on conifers and preferring the deciduous forests and glades where they feed together, walking over the ground taking worms, insects, berries and seeds. Owing, however, to large scale forest destruction, management and exploitation, the

AMERICAN TURKEY *(Meleagris gallopavo gallopavo)*   7.1

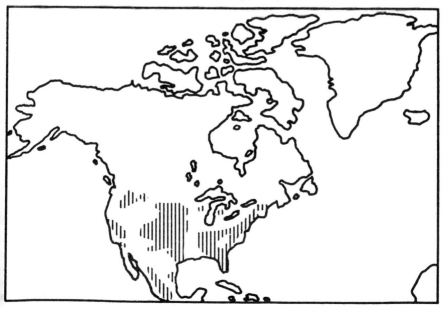

Turkey is now greatly restricted. What is being done to Turkey habitat by modern Americans is the same as their ancestors did to the Capercaillies' habitat before emigrating to North America.

Voice The Turkey's *'gobble gobble'* needs little explanation. Domestication certainly has not diminished the call either.

Display Mature cocks display with fanned out tails and puffed up wattles. Displaying takes place on the ground and hens when stimulated move in to the cock of their choosing for mating, after which they return to their nests.

Breeding After mating the hen selects her nest site on the ground, hidden under a bush or in long vegetation. This is no more than a scrape, with little effort at lining it. The hen will lay from 15–20 eggs, buff in colour and spotted. These eggs are incubated for 28 days, the chicks being light fawn with brown spots.

Aviculture Not commonly kept now although formerly quite popular and, in fact, naturalised in Germany for sporting purposes. There is no great difficulty with this bird although if kept in a restricted area Blackhead is likely to strike. Wild Turkeys can be allowed to free range and forage with around one cock to three hens. The young have a high protein requirement and need to be well supplied with protein pellets and/or meal worms and greenfood. When fledged a diet of mixed grains is adequate for maintenance although Turkey Breeder Pellets are advisable in the spring. Where kept in close confinement hens must be given the opportunity to escape the cock or they can suffer nasty scarring on their backs from the cocks' spurs. In extreme cases the birds fail to incubate properly due to this disturbance from an over-zealous cock.

Sub-species Several have been described but to what extent they are valid is open to question and when there was a continuous distribution they probably integrated to a large extent.

Eastern Turkey *M.g. silvestris;* located in Kentucky, West Virginia, Missouri and Pennsylvania.
Chestnut upper tail covers and tips to the rectrices.

Rio Grande Turkey *M.g. intermedial*, South Eastern Texas and adjacent Mexican region.
Black rump with cinnamon — buff upper tail coverts.

Florida Turkey *M.g. osceola.*
Smaller with no barring on inner secondaries and shorter white bars on the primaries.

Moores Turkey *M.g. onusta.* Western Sierra Madre from Chihuahua and Sonora to Jalisco.
No white tip to tail feathers which are also barred, not mottled.

Gould's Turkey *M.g. mexicana.* Eastern Sierra Madre from Chihuahua to Jalisco.
Larger than the nominate race, similarly marked but with more of a metallic hue rather than the blue on the lower back and rump.

Merriam's Turkey *M.g. merriami,* scattered through New Mexico, Eastern Arizona and Southern Colorado.
Upper tail coverts white as are the tips of the rectices.

Sharptailed Grouse

Chapter 4

Gamebirds
in Aviculture

The rearing of birds in numbers for shooting, though this activity is not precisely aviculture as the term is generally accepted, contains the most essential basics of husbandry for propagation of birds. The species most common are True Pheasants, Grey Partridges and Red Legged Partridges. More recently the Rock Partridges and Common Quails have also been added to the list of intensively reared species.

Prior to shooting requirements creating a demand for captively reared birds of the Gallinaceous type, we can go back in history to those reared especially for the table, as far back as Roman or probably pre-Roman times. The most likely species is the Caucasian Pheasant, whose westward distribution by Man arose out of this practice after the inevitable escapees established, themselves throughout the former Roman Empire including the cleared forest areas under agriculture in Southern England. In all probability the methods adopted were the fostering of eggs from the wild for that purpose, placing them under the related domestic fowl originating itself in the wild from the Indian sub-continent.

From the foregoing it is quite obvious that Man has had a fairly long established relationship with Gallinaceous birds; for a very long time indeed, if we consider the Chinese Art depicting 'fowls' of very ancient origin, very accurately depicted on silk tens of thousands of years ago. I do not think, however, that going this far back is germain to what is to be considered in this section of the book, nor would it have practical benefits for our purposes.

Undoubtedly propagation of True Pheasants is well documented and has been widely practiced throughout Europe for some two thousand years. Eggs of all bird species were collected, and even in my youth still were used as a food resource. Nowadays this is largely restricted to seabirds and to a lesser extent waterfowl. Relative universal affluence and urbanisation, with a corresponding human population explosion, no longer makes this practical.

Prior to the firearm era, rearing of Pheasants was almost exclusively for the culinary benefit of the very rich and, invariably, land owning households. It was always a luxury even for these people and was most likely never more than a minority activity delegated to someone capable of finding one or two clutches of eggs, initially just of Pheasants but then latterly of Common or Grey Partridges. These were set under any available and suitably broody Fowls who would be largely responsible for hatching and then rearing to poult size those chicks delegated to that particular hen. The advent of firearms of a reliable and accurate type brought about radical changes as far as rearing gamebirds is concerned in terms of scale, resources applied, and latterly geographically. It is easy to be disparaging and describe the methods used as crude, but it is well worth remembering that not only were 'haybox' incubators used successfully when 'broody' hens were wanting in numbers or reliability. Under both systems diseases were overcome, as was inclement weather, and a previously very high level of predation by species of mammals and birds greatly which reduced the numbers and in some cases exterminated them.

Despite all these 'improvements' to which one can now add enormous incubators capable of hatching thousands of birds each, plus modern medications, housing, brooding and other advantages, the tidings of great woe are louder than before, especially with the True Pheasants now often confusingly hybridised. Why should this be? What has gone wrong and who is to blame? To all but the most unobservant it must be obvious that we are to blame, of course. As with many other species of animal we have domesticated this Pheasant, or nearly so. 'Flight response', when confronted by predators either winged or legged, has been dulled if not extinguished. Fertility is also impaired, and this can happen very quickly. Egg sizes and shapes vary enormously and this must be negative. Abnormal colour variations are occurring naturally and regularly, as happened long ago with the domestic Fowl. Another not infrequent occurrence is the appearance of hermaphrodites.

All these variations are not associated with natural speciation, nor do they improve natural survival; mortality is quite the reverse under semi-natural conditions. This all poses a highly pertinent and important question which simply put is: how does the modern aviculturalist avoid the risks of domestication amongst those species with which he chooses to work? We have already witnessed the appearance of more than one mutation of the Golden Pheasant. In certain quarters this is hailed as a triumph, which it most certainly is not. They are freaks, and arose through the path travelled by a species being domesticated. This surely cannot be what aviculture proper is about. These mutations should be treated as what they are — freaks. Proportionately speaking, for such a species as the Golden Pheasant, this is not a threat as such, but in the author's view it is the attitude of mind amongst those who seek to produce such obvious freaks which is suspect. Logically, according to mathematical probability further oddities of this type will appear in this species quite soon, and the absence of albinism at this time seems surprising.

Aviculture has already an important role in preserving species of all forms of birds from extermination and will, in future, be vital in this respect. This is where the ordinary, concerned individual has also a role to play. Perhaps at this juncture it is worth clarifying the correct definition in English of the terms 'extinct' and 'exterminated'. To become extinct a species must, through its own evolutionary failure, have arrived naturally at a blind alley. It is reasonable to assume that, while perhaps Man may be involved to some degree, he is not responsible! To be exterminated' a species, through no fault of its own, can be said to have been destroyed by Man and we are responsible most emphatically for that. It is to this latter category that aviculturalists should address themselves, at least in part, during the forthcoming decades.

We all, aviculturally, have to start somewhere. It obviously would be not only stupid but also imprudent for beginners to be allowed near endangered or rare species, and those with a serious concern for their role in future conservation would themselves agree that they would be better learning their basics and making their mistakes with those species commonly available. Birds of such common species are readily available as is, in my experience, advice right across the board from scientists, gifted amateurs and wealthy enthusiasts. It would be well worth according credit where it is most due. With the limited exception of a very few scientists, results from time and money spent are most consistently obtained by gifted amateurs, and not only in respect of Gallinaceous birds.

In Western Europe and North America the back-yard is indeed a productive place, which is probably just as well as it is from these societies we also find the greatest threats generated to all species and their habitats. Unfortunately it is not quite 'quid pro quo' but we will all just have to try harder as no-one can seriously doubt our ability to do so provided the will is there. Aviculturalists are the base-line. It is from this position that time can be bought while each species can be studied in depth, their needs determined and their habitats secured and/or re-established.

In the Galliformes group there are extensive challenges still waiting for people from all points of interest, and while most of us understand this point to some extent it has to be said that there is a body in each of the main disciplines which tends to be disparaging about the efforts of others not in fact walking their path. The ornithologists have to remember the hunting lobby is the originator of methods now used to save species past and present from extermination. The hunters must give an ear to the ecologists' views as it is from their efforts we now know so much, although a great deal remains to be done. Aviculturalists must keep track of developments and new techniques; they must also keep their feet on the ground and clarify their own role. Lastly, and equally important, the public must make it their business with their new mobility and demands on the environment through need for access and resources, to try and obtain some perception of what is being attempted by the others and the role they have in supporting, encouraging and lobbying the powers that be to these ends for everyone's mutual benefit, wherever their interests may lie.

Before World War II, gamebirds in aviculture were usually in the hands of a limited number of highly motivated people who were fortunate to have the financial resources to pursue this interest and to do so well; perhaps never so well as Dr. Jean Delacour in France who, after that unhappy episode in Europe's history, has started all over again showing us all how the job should and can be done. It is an extremely difficult job for anyone to walk in his shadow, let alone fill his shoes. He is a classic example of an enthusiastic amateur who achieved things by 'feel', and all without the aid of facilities modern aviculturalists now can call upon. What Delacour achieved, and continues to achieve, with Sub-Tropical and Tropical species remains to be achieved with the Grouse and, outside the scope of this book, the Cracids of South America. Other notable post-war aviculturalists include Charles Seville of the United States, Wolfgang Aschenbrenner of Germany and recently people like Iain Grahame, Christopher Savage, Keith Howman, Jack Killeen, and others in the UK ploughing new furrows.

Perhaps because of the specialised expertise needed, very few bird gardens or zoos have much success with species other than the relatively easy to maintain ones, which is to the eternal credit of the 'backyarder' and a reflection on so called 'modern' zoos.

Later in this part of the book I propose to try and record some of the things which are now being done in aviculture, how they are achieved and under what conditions, as they affect those species previously described here. To do this will require detailed consideration of various methods used by different people as part of their husbandry, under varying conditions such as rainfall, temperature ranges, soil type, local vegetation and so forth. There is no 'best' system specific to any one species other than that of its natural biological status in the wild and it therefore follows that the balance of probability would suggest the next best compromise is most likely to be artificial by varying degrees and it is in the skill of the aviculturalist that we find the best modifications to achieve sustained, or better still, surplus, healthy populations.

An obvious extra dimension is where we can take, as aviculturalists, the requirements of the previous chapter and add that piece of finesse, landscaping. In itself a well landscaped aviary adds much to the pleasure and enjoyment of working with our chosen birds. There is another, often overlooked or at best poorly understood, aspect to landscaping. While such a well thought-out aviary may be aesthetically pleasing to the human eye, it does greatly enhance the quality of life for the birds themselves and this is worth looking at closely in the following sections.

Chapter 4.1

Aviary Planning and Construction

Before anyone makes a move to keep livestock obviously they have to have somewhere to accommodate whatever it is planned to acquire. For many types of birds native to the Temperate Boreal Zone, keeping them in captivity is not terribly difficult anywhere within that same zone, with their being naturally acclimatised. Gallinaceous birds have their own special demands and should the aviculturalist be fortunate enough to start from scratch as it were, this is a significant bonus as it allows for a disease-free situation and purpose-built aviary or aviaries. This does not mean, however, that existing premises cannot be adapted, but this section of the book works from the standpoint of a clear site and leaves the reader to work around this as he sees fit in relation to the area he or she may have to work with.

Starting with a bare site, it is essential to consider access for materials to be delivered on site. Pushing endless wheelbarrows full of sand, gravel and rock is not much fun on a level site and it is bad if wet and muddy, and nearly impossible uphill. So, having decided you want an aviary, check next to see if the chosen site has practical access for the heavy stuff!

Other vital points common to all species, which must be checked, include:—
1. Wind directions, strength and frequency.
2. Quantity and periodicity of rainfall.
3. Depth and consequentially the weight of snow to be expected on roof netting, and/or drifting, in relation to perch positions.

4. Soil type, acidity and natural drainage.
5. Direction of slope especially in regard to all of the above.
6. Natural shade from adjacent trees or buildings, if any.
7. Natural shelter, if any, from the prevaling elements.
8. Likelihood of cats or dogs wandering past at ground level.
9. Proximity to other potentially aggressive birds.
10. Whether birds are monogamous or polygamous.
11. Whether terrestial or arboreal.
12. Whether natural or artificial incubation is planned.
13. Whether birds are vegetarian exclusively, or partially.
14. Is it planned to have the birds on public display?
15. Where are the birds to be kept during cleaning or maintenance?
16. Are there any height considerations or limitations?
17. What avian or mammalian predators are there to contend with?

These are some of the basic considerations which need to be looked at as a preliminary before work can even start on sketching a simple design which can be worked up into something upon which decisions can be made.

We all have our individual perceptions of aesthetics, but while it is perhaps more common to find aviaries either individually or in a series of rectangular shapes this seems a shame. Purely as a personal view, there is so much more which can be done with a little imagination in regard to irregular shapes. Associated with this opinion is the need to prevent abnormal behaviour, such as displacement pacing which can develop. Other advantages in irregular shape are the reduction of feather damage to long-tailed species and the avoidance, at least in part, of aggression sometimes by cocks on their own hens, who when they are brooding, appear to the cock to be soliciting copulation. This eventually leads to abandoning the clutch and even damage to eggs. If the human eye is intimidated by the sight of seried rows of aviaries imagine what it must be like for a confined wild creature. Remember, contented birds are productive and relatively more successful as well.

Availability of certain types of material must be considered, along with relevant costs, as must ease of access for unrestricted movement when undertaking routine maintenance. This is prudent planning and husbandry; for example, porous rocks harbour infection. Replacement sand taken in by the bucketful when it can be lobbed in through the front, and perches old and new removed and replaced this way all make for an easier life. Timber treated with preservatives under pressure is more expensive initially, but is a substantial saving in the long-term when used for framing. It also has the advantage of being resistent to parasites which could be potentially harmful to the birds themselves. It has to be said, however, that there is one exhibition aviary in the National Park of Bavaria where construction is largely by means of logs, and it is of a very impressive nature, being set in Pine Forest and curved, although in series. Catching up birds in an aviary introduces an element of stress which can be avoided if a 'shift' cage at the rear can be incorporated into which they can be temporarily shut during cleaning or maintenance operations. This would apply whether the birds are in exhibition or simpler breeding aviaries. Obviously there will be some aviaries which will be used either solely for breeding 'off limits' and/or for behaviour studies, in which case certain other considerations in design will also apply according to these specific needs.

With a site chosen to take advantage of the most sheltered aspect, and equal attention being paid to sound soil drainage, which can be improved by increased depths of gravel or other substrata covered by sand, we can go on to consider a number of other important aspects before even picking up the spade. The first of these must be the birds themselves. We have to consider if they are inherently aggressive or not; are they large in size or otherwise; are they monogamous or polygamous; do they lek display, and where do they roost? Answers to these questions are utterly fundamental when considering size, layout and interior design for the many various species.

Because of the hardiness of the species covered by this book one aspect does not need to be considered here, and that is artificial heat, but it should be borne in mind if more southerly species are being contemplated. Nevertheless, what is often overlooked is the suscepti-bility of all species to chill caused by draughts. A species may be as tough as old boots in the wild, but in confinement the birds may not be able to avoid draughts in a badly laid-out or poorly constructed aviary. To avoid some of the draughts, and panic or alarm amongst birds due to passing cats or dogs, aviaries should really have a solid front from ground level to a height of at least 60cm for smaller species or 90cm for the larger species. These ground level barriers are also useful on the sides, especially as visual barriers separating birds in adjacent aviaries, and are often necessary in preventing fighting.

Also, when wind direction changes, they act as additional screens behind which the birds may seek protection.

To the rear of an aviary a solid wall, constructed by whatever means, is highly desirable for a number of reasons, including total rain and wind protection and a secure visual barrier against disturbance or imagined threat as perceived by the birds. Additionally, at least part if not all of this area should be covered in some way to prevent rain and disturbance from avian or the more agile mammalian predators, especially when birds are roosting.

At this juncture it may be helpful if the reasons are set out for dwelling on the 'disturbance' factor amongst captive birds. We all would agree that captivity is an unnatural state and we are dealing with wild birds all of whom have the characteristic of extremely rapid speeds in take off and flight which, on account of size, can cause severe injury if not actual death. Animal behaviourists studying what is called 'flight response', have calculated that each species of animal and bird has a number of reaction distances in which they regard the presence of a predator as: ignorable, in need of wariness, and in need of flight. This latter distance is known as the 'flight distance' and exists for every species, including Man. It is the point beyond which an approaching threat triggers the change from a leisurely retreat, i.e. walking away, to − in the case of birds − taking to the wing, and for unpinioned gamebirds this is fast!

It must be apparent from the above that the depth of an aviary front to back must be greater than the width. Effectively this allows a bird feeling apprehensive to retreat perhaps to the halfway point and feel secure enough at the rear to nest and roost. The stress factor is something of extreme importance to any species, captive or otherwise, and can lead to abnormal displacement behaviour such as pacing, feather picking, and so forth, which can lead to death at worst, or inhibitions that prevent breeding which after all is, or should be, the name of the game. As far as height of an aviary is concerned, this can vary according to whether a species is terrestial, i.e. preferring to roost on perhaps a large rock or some other prominent object placed on the aviary floor. If, however, a species is arboreal in nature, it will need to be provided with roosting perches such as branches at a reasonable height to give the birds a feeling of security which is essential to avoid needless stress.

Whatever type of species one keeps, the roosting is most likely to take place out of choice at the rear of an aviary. Again, to avoid stress, consideration must be given to what material is used to cover the roof in this area. By varying degree aviculturalists have to contend with intruders frightening their birds. This disturbance may take many forms, from the neighbour's prowling cat along the rear or sides to opportunist urban or rural foxes looking in, as do some domestic dogs and even badgers. I have to contend with wildcats, pinemartins, polecats, foxes, badgers, and perhaps the most disturbing of all, birds of prey, either flying over low or, especially with owls, sitting on the actual aviary. The two species which cause me greatest difficulty are Peregrines and Buzzards, but other birds such as Harriers and Barn Owls make life difficult, especially amongst Poults. In Scandinavia and Germany another species which is a substantial problem is the Goshawk.

When deciding on wire mesh sizes for outside fences, dimensions must be chosen for their ability to keep out animals such as pinemartins, polecats, stoats, weasels and, despite one's best endeavours,

Figure 8. **Aviary Layout**

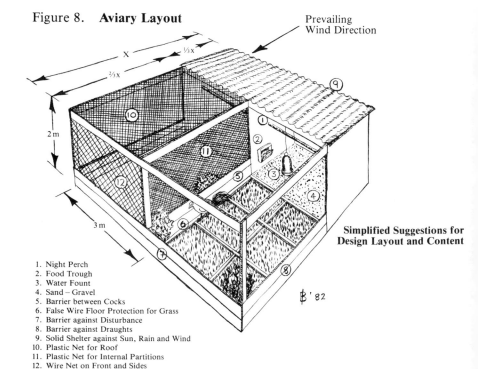

Prevailing
Wind Direction

**Simplified Suggestions for
Design Layout and Content**

1. Night Perch
2. Food Trough
3. Water Fount
4. Sand – Gravel
5. Barrier between Cocks
6. False Wire Floor Protection for Grass
7. Barrier against Disturbance
8. Barrier against Draughts
9. Solid Shelter against Sun, Rain and Wind
10. Plastic Net for Roof
11. Plastic Net for Internal Partitions
12. Wire Net on Front and Sides

the rat, who will come calling eventually. At least one aviculturalist I know of, Ursula Wilmering in Germany, keeps the larger Grouse species in large, open-topped enclosures as pinioned birds but, much as I would like to do this, it would be impossible on account of the various predators mentioned, plus the egg destruction which would result from visits by Ravens and Hooded Crows, not to mention what would happen to chicks and poults after Greater and Lesser Black Backed Gulls and the Falcons turned their attention on them during early summer. To each his own; not for me the open topped aviary, although I would very much like to try it.

Various types of wire mesh are available, either as 'chicken wire' made in differing widths, wire thicknesses and net dimensions, or as the 'weldmesh' type, again differing in width, wire thickness and net dimensions, which are in this type rectangular. The 'chicken mesh' type is made of galvanised wire and unless regularly painted degrades rather too quickly for my liking. If it is painted with black enamel the effect is rather pleasing and appears to visually dissolve the wire while also making for longer life. This wire is not very effective against a determined predator such as a fox or a badger, though wildcats, martins and polecats cannot damage it; but beware the mesh size is not too large or they will walk right through. When buried, this type of netting degrades very quickly and it is not recommended for this purpose. One of the apparent advantages of chicken mesh over the 'weldmesh' type is cost per square metre, but this is rather deceptive as the latter type is very much more long-lasting even in its more narrow gauges, and all the more so if protectively painted or obtained plastic covered at higher cost either in black or green plastic. This is the type I personally prefer. Black is the best, as green surprisingly is not so good from the camouflage point of view. One further type of netting is the polypropolene woven net which usually is supplied in black. This is actually a very useful type of netting for use particularly with gamebirds as, while it was initially used to cover Pheasant release pens where birds are reared for shooting, it has now also been shown to be equally useful between adjacent aviaries or on aviary sides and even front panels. Apart from the obvious ease and speed of use, this netting is light and can carry a substantial weight of snow, sagging rather than breaking. Should birds in the aviaries be panicked and fly into this netting it will 'give' and serious injuries can be avoided as a result. Another interesting property is a sort of 'trampoline' effect which must come as something of a shock to a Peregrine in full stoop on the birds inside. I often wonder what they think as they hurtle back upwards. This netting is very strong as the author has had a newly installed pair of Eagle Owls hanging upside down together from one panel of an aviary. If one can be sure of minimal vandalism associated with well supervised aviaries it is well worth considering on the front as well as the roof and sides.

For that part of the aviary roof which is weather-proofed a variety of materials are now available, including timber covered by tarred roofing felt, and corrugated composite roofing felt which is also available in a clear perspex material that excludes rain but admits light. This new corrugated material is a great advance on the tradiitional corrugated iron sheets which have many drawbacks, not the least of which is corrosion. It is not likely to cause injury and as a roofing material it does not, during rain storms, end up sounding like sitting in a noisy barrel, all of which makes for a more congenial environment. Another advantage is that it is light and easily handled, even being able to be cut by an ordinary saw either to reduce its two metre length or trim edges at an angle to allow turning corners of aviaries which are of an irregular shape.

As far as aviary floors are concerned, this is an area which requires a great deal of thought. It is perhaps the most important part of an area in which Gamebirds are kept, with hygiene particularly important as a consideration, so prone can these birds be to self-infection and even cross-infection, e.g. Avian T.B. from droppings falling through the roof netting, released by wild birds perching there. There are a number of different flooring types used throughout the world and the principal ones are listed with comments on their advantages or disadvantages:

Concrete   This is easily cleaned by hosing it down and it lends itself readily to sterilising. Aesthetically, however, it leaves a lot to be desired and is perhaps only acceptable for certain species kept solely for study purposes, in a sick-bay or in quarantine. One variation on this has large and small rocks imbedded in the concrete with a further permutation of a thin layer of sand on top as well. However, this set-up is very frustrating for Pheasant species which are inclined to dig; there is also a risk of foot lesions over a prolonged period which can cause lameness or serious infection. Birds are unlikely to breed under such conditions and I would advise against using this arrangement except during isolation for limited periods. A rather expensive floor.

Suspended Wire Floors   These are frequently used under laboratory conditions and for over-wintering birds to rest the soil and break the cycle of pest infestations. Some aviculturalists do use this system as a permanent one for all types of Gamebirds including Partridges, Quail, Grouse and Francolins. Some of them, like Partridges, are managed this way intensively for commercial reasons. Personally, I see nothing of merit in this. It is something of a lazy man's unimaginative method for exploiting these birds, and is only a short step removed from battery farming, which is the extreme form of this system and which most sane people condemn anyway, and rightly so. The only circumstances in which I would use this procedure would be for quarantining birds or as a hospital cage for treatment over short periods when it can be of benefit to the birds.

Grounded Wire Floors   This system fits into an aviary over all or part of the grassed area with the wire stretched over framing 5.1cm/ 2 inches square. This has the effect both of keeping the birds free of most of their own or other birds droppings and consequential risks of infection while also allowing the grass to maintain growth which the birds crop as it comes through. An added advantage in areas of poor soil drainage is that the birds are kept out of the damp and also they do not uproot the grass. This is especially important with species prone to digging, such as the Eared Pheasants. This system is often used in conjunction with adjacent areas which are sanded. The netted areas can be worked in around shrubbery and other landscaping features. Choice of wire here is important. If the mesh is too wide this causes stress on the toes and legs; if the gauge is too thin the life of the floor is dramatically shortened. Ideally the wire should be 1.3cm/½ inch thick and plastic-coated for a prolonged life. The wooden framing must be treated with preservative or some sort, ideally under one of the pressure treatment systems. If done well this type of flooring quickly blends into the aviary and makes a safe and practical solution, if somewhat costly by comparison with other alternatives.

Deep Litter   This type of floor has both advantages and disadvantages, and is used for rearing Quail commercially. The medium for litter is granulated peat as obtained for use by gardeners. For birds on public display this system has its limitations, requiring periodic changes and it is rather labour intensive. One advantage is that peat is sterile, and spread to a depth of 5.1cm/2 inches it can be kept in reasonable condition longer by periodic raking over. A new alternative becoming more readily available is tree bark litter which, especially for forest species, is rather appropriate and pleasing to the eye when spread to the same depth as peat.

Both types of litter allow for landscaping and have a worthwhile spin-off, especially for the keen gardeners, providing well fertilised humous of benefit to all. Cost-wise this is a reasonable flooring medium, especially as both types are re-usable as mentioned above. An essential factor to be considered before using the litter systems is that there must be a good and well drained sub-strata either naturally or by adding a rubble or rock layer to a depth of 15.2cm/6 inches.

Sand   One of the commonest methods, mainly due I suppose to readily available material at a reasonable cost. This system is very effective in eliminating dampness and as sand is fairly sterile, invertibrates which act as vectors (for example, the Gapeworm), find it an unattractive environment. Depending on natural soil type and drainage it may be advisable to put down a rock base to a depth of 15.3cm/ 2 inches. For landscaping, water-worn rock can be scattered irregularly throughout the aviary to effect. Periodically the sand can be limed with garden lime to control any toxicity which might develop. It also helps break down bird droppings more rapidly, reducing potential for infection and re-infection. One of the benefits of a sand base is that the birds can indulge in frequent dust bathing. It also ensures adequate grit for the crops of those species most in need of it, particularly all the Grouse family. Probably, however, such a floor is not the best by any means for any of the grazing species.

Grass and Pasture   This floor type has much to commend it, but it is restricted to certain species only, and anyway requires careful management, usually only gained from experience. It is practised to a fine art, perhaps best of all, by Ursala Wilmering in Germany. Certain aspects have to be just right. The density of bird population is most important and this is dictated by grass species, soil type, rainfall and absence of predators. The three species of Grouse which would probably benefit most would be the Sharp Tailed, Pinnated and Black Grouse, while amongst the Pheasants all three Eared Pheasants would benefit too. Perhaps this type could be managed in conjunction with one of the others, using grass from March/April through to September/October at which time the birds could be shifted to winter quarters.

No doubt there are alternatives to the above used by others success-fully, but the examples quoted give sufficient understanding of the possibilities and their attendant benefits and problems. Now it is necessary to consider the landscaping of an aviary, sometimes not wholly inappropriately referred to as 'the furniture'. It is my firm view that not nearly enough attention is paid to landscaping by very many aviculturists, many of whom often are guilty of making a large, or not so large, wire basket and sticking in a couple of birds and a box. Being quite blunt, anyone can manage that much. It surely is not being unduly altruistic to make the aviary interesting for the observer and the observed.

No one can deny the thrill on seeing first thing in the morning a Hen bird crouched away from her nest site while a few chicks stumble in and out from under her loosely fluffed feathers. This is not being sentimental – it is what we wait for every year and while any well-housed and fed bird can produce, she is more likely to do so in an environment which is as near as we can make it to the natural, and therefore secure enough for her to try herself. I fully expect disagree-ment with the following statement by many, but the author firmly believes that the higher the standard an aviculturist reaches the less he relies on an incubator and brooder to produce his young birds. If we could all aim at that and, more importantly, achieve it, the 'craft' will have moved forward mightily.

A well landscaped or 'furnished' aviary is a pre-requisite on the road to achieving the highest aims. This means nesting cover dis-creetly placed and coloured to suit the hen's markings in more than one location. It also means a display log if the cock is that kind of a fellow, or alternatively an area to show off in if he needs it, or perhaps he likes to show off in front of his fellow birds. It all has to be thought out carefully. We need to know if the hen needs to escape from the cock, or does he attend her during brooding? What is the attitude of the cock to his offspring when they hatch? Do the birds roost on the ground, in cover, just off the ground or higher up? Questions all needing answers, and these decide what is included or omitted.

One of the objectives of landscaping and layout is to stimulate and exercise the birds of both sexes. If flight is restricted then perches must be placed high enough to induce reasonable exertion without strain. Other points to bear in mind include removal of bark from perches, as this harbours pests, and barkless timber can be disinfected more readily. Do not leave uninterrupted walkways; break up these lines with rocks or shrubbery, especially alongside walls, as this eliminates stereotyped displacement behaviour before it gets a chance to become established. In the company of unusually aggressive cocks, hens need secure retreats to escape, e.g. a crouching incubating hen could be misinterpreted by the cock as sexually soliciting and, apart from the risk of a scarred back through treading, the extra weight leads to broken eggs and the Hen going off brooding, all because of a lack of forethought.

General comments on construction principles are worth considering here as they contribute to future levels of the maintenance, stability and useful life of the structure, and finally the frequency with which one must physically enter an aviary with the consequential disturbance of the occupants that this involves. In some cases certain species are very confiding and a familiar person popping in and out is not in any way detrimental to the birds or their inclination to nest and incubate, but the very opposite can be said of a cock Capercaillie in full display when one can expect to be physically attacked, which might sound amusing but is not! These birds know how to rough it and are big enough to make an impression physically and literally. The timber I use is all preserved by pressure treatment when sawn, or otherwise is exterior grade marine plywood. If possible nails and staples are hot dipped galvanised as are hinges and latches. When using bolts rather than nails for framing I try to cover the nuts with grease on completion. I live in an area of extreme rainfall and high wind, the latter having a mean annual speed of 35 miles/56km per hour gusting to 80 miles/129km per hour and sometimes in excess of this. I therefore have to build with an eye on basic engineering as well as aesthetics or, as has happened, I can find aviaries twisted, flattened, doors blown in – or out, or simply no aviary left at all. It is essential, therefore, to back all my aviaries into the wind with a lower profile on that side rising to the front and screened by planting trees for shelter in the long-term at the back, using various species including fast-growing tall trees and low-growing shrubs.

My soil is very shallow and poorly drained, so as a rule the aviaries all have a gravel base covered by sand, although a few are grassed on a thin soil over gravel. Around the base of all the aviaries is a section either of buried wire or packed rock to discourage foxes, badgers and others. This precaution is vital, especially in remote mountain areas such as that in which I live. Foxes are now fairly common everywhere, especially so nowadays in urban areas. It is therefore advisable for everyone keeping birds which are as attractive meal-wise for predators as Gamebirds are, to consider the eventual likelihood of a visitor who might want to get in. More likely and more frequently aviculturalists can expect the patter of little feet with various mice, voles and rats finding the food interesting, and during the breeding season the eggs are also a potential target. Thought has to be given to how food is supplied within the aviary having regard to attracting rodents if it is too accessible. Also, there is the problem of spillage being spoilt through contact with the floor before being eaten. It is also important to keep it dry.

Another and very important factor in relation to food is the problem of avoiding entry to the aviary while still having access for cleaning food vessels and replenishing them when necessary. A possible solution is incorporating this requirement for limited access by means of a trap-door or hinged flap located on the rear wall of the aviaries. The feed dispenser, of whatever type chosen, can be located on a shelf raised to a reasonable height, allowing birds access to food, grit and water. Where possible there is a considerable merit in suspending these dispensers from under the covered part of the aviary roof. This has the benefit of keeping everything dry and reduces risk of contamination from rodents and droppings falling from birds perched on the roof netting elsewhere. By operating feeding access points in this way feeding and watering can be completed much more quickly. It also minimises disturbance, particularly if aviaries are in series.

It is hoped that the foregoing, along with the associated diagrams and photographs, may help anyone contemplating aviary construction to decide on an aviary which can be made to suit the available site and intended occupants, while also serving as a generally interesting feature that the owner would be proud to show anyone at any time, however unexpected that visitor might be, and if the aviary is not normally seen by the public. Finally I would make a plea for fewer aviaries and better ones, more spacious and interesting, from which all can take pleasure, not the least of which, of course, being the occupants.

Chapter 4.2
Aviary Plants
and Shrubs

As emphasised earlier, there are two reasons for an aviary being well planted. The obvious aesthetic appeal is uppermost in the human mind and eye but equally, and more serious, is the tremendous value and importance to the birds' well-being, especially amongst those species most prone to stress. Other very important reasons include the need to break up straight lines in an aviary which does a great deal to avoid displacement behaviour such as pacing and leg lifting against the sides which is brought on by the bird's attempts to climb over obstacles in an effort to either retreat or escape. There is also the need to provide shade for some species and seclusion for egg laying and later brooding if need be. Eggs deposited just anywhere can attract attention from the Cock if he is bored, and this can develop into breakage through pecking and even eating.

All of the above reasons are at least enough to make the caring and serious aviculturists sit down and put some serious and considered thought into this subject, owing to its obviously considerable importance and contribution to success. Nothing in life is simple, regardless of what paths we choose to follow, and selecting suitable plants for an aviary is confoundedly difficult. Some of the earliest points which must be considered are those listed below:–

1.   Are the birds fond of certain plant types and likely to eat them?
2.   Would either the foliage or fruits prove poisonous to the birds if eaten by them?

3. What effect would the acidity or alkalinity of the soil (known as soil p.h.) have on each plant species' growth?
4. Of necessity aviary soil conditions must err on the dry side rather than the wet, so would a chosen plant species grow under these conditions?
5. Does the plant like direct light or shade and can it tolerate shade?
6. What effects would temperature extremes have on growth or survival of the plants? Something which grows well on the Scottish West Coast may not do very well, if it grows at all, in the South of France.
7. Will the plant need pruning or other sorts of maintenance, and how often?
8. Does the plant grow in a spreading manner, and does this matter?
9. How high will it grow, and how fast? If it grows too high too quickly it will become a nuisance, damaging both the aviary and perhaps other plants through competition for light and nutrients. Alternatively, if it grows high but slowly then it may outlive the life of the aviary and could prove very useful.

Before applying too much thought to the above perhaps it would be useful to quickly and briefly consider how 'purist' one wishes to be. By this I mean does the aviculturist wish to grow, in association with his birds, examples of plants found growing naturally within that bird's native region? I pose the question because there is seemingly a great deal of merit in this, in that it creates a balanced perspective between the birds and their surroundings. This is especially important as some, including myself, take the view that where, for example, birds are on display to the public a much better grasp can be had by visitors as to the natural setting for that species. To take a ridiculous but perfectly likely pair of examples, it would be rather unsubtle to stick Capercaillie in an aviary which includes a very large rhododendron, and likewise with one of the Eared Pheasants in an aviary with a Stunted Pine, when with a little thought they could be better accommodated by switching aviaries.

Equally, one does understand, with difficulty, that there are those who are content to utilise any plant species providing it will grow. One feels a great opportunity, and it could be said a challenge, has been missed in this case, which would be a pity. In choosing aviary plants there are some obvious pitfalls, and some not so obvious ones. These include root damage by birds which habitually dig, such as the Eared Pheasants. This can be overcome with a few flat rocks or stones close to, but not against, the plant. There is also the problem of birds trying to perch on branches not yet able to take their weight. However, suitably placed perches will reduce this if not entirely cure it.

From a purely Avicultural point of view, if one has a bird species which is naturally shy and habitually uses cover in which to hide, then by all means increase the availability of suitable plants. It is important to remember that where birds are on view to the public this can be overdone and the birds, especially hens, of sexually dimorphic species, are never seen. While we may be practised in picking her out, the vast majority do not have a clue − literally and metaphorically. It might be worth citing an instance of this which I experienced with some of my own birds. A hen Caucasian Pheasant chose to nest under a Bramble bush one metre from the front of her aviary, and during her three weeks 'on the pot' literally thousands of people walked past her without seeing her at all and constantly asked, "haven't you got a mate for the Cock Pheasant?" We would say yes and explain; some would go away in total disbelief muttering, "nothing wrong with my eyes", but others would return for another try and be staggered and amazed when they came back to the entrance. Somewhere along the line a balance has to be chosen. The question of course is where, and everyone has his ideas on that. Let us be honest and admit that there are some people who would fail to see an Albino Peacock on its own in the middle of a tarmacadamed car park. What was it that chap said − "you can please some of the people some of the time but not all of the people all of the time".

To try and assist the reader in choosing possible aviary plants a few species are tabulated along with some of their characteristics which might simplify things and make choosing easier. Obviously some plants may or may not be locally available or be absent in certain countries; similarly, on a cautionary note, it is the case that in certain countries there exists legislation protecting wild plants. In the case of Scotland and England, for example, some plants may not be removed under any circumstances and all other plants only with the consent of the owner of the land on which the plant or plants grow. It is well worth asking permission, because when the reason is given you may find more help forthcoming than you imagined.

This has been my experience and it is invariably true that local knowledge can save you a lot of time and even lead to better or more easily accessible specimens.

It is advisable when choosing plants to try and include some which are evergreen as this makes for a more visually pleasing aviary during the long winter months. Another extremely important factor is to grade the vegetation by height from lowest to highest, front to back and, in the case of especially large and wide aviaries, from the centre to the sides. This is essential to avoid 'losing' the rear of the aviaries and also their birds after the plants establish themselves.

The following is a table of some plant species which may prove useful:—

Grouse

Suitable Trees and Shrubs for Aviaries

SPECIES	Height	Growth	Shade	Colour	Comments
1. Norway Spruce *Picea abies prostrata and compressa*	3 m	slow	tolerant	green	the nominate form is much too fast growing for aviaries
2. White Spruce (Black Hills) *Picea glauca densata*	7 m	slow	tolerant	green	the nominate form is much too fast growing for aviaries
3. Colorado Spruce *Picea pungens compacta*	3 m	slow	tolerant	green	the nominate form is much too fast growing for aviaries
4. Swiss Stone Pine *Pinus cembra*	10 m	slow	intolerant	green	greater heights are ultimately possible after many years
5. Macedonian Pine *Pinus peuce*	10 m	slow	intolerant	green	similar to *Pinus cembra*, with large yellow cones
6. Jack Pine *Pinus banksiana*	10 m	slow	intolerant	green	eventually in time exceeds 10m
7. Swiss Mountain Pine *Pinus mugo*	6 m	very slow	intolerant	green	shrubby, almost prostrate; looks good in groups
8. Scots Pine *Pinus sylvestris*	15 m	moderate	intolerant	green	can exceed size quoted but can be easily 'shruberised'
9. Ginkgo *Ginkgo biloba*	15 m	moderate	intolerant	green deciduous conifer	rather irregular in shape; can be pruned in time
10. American Larch *Larix laricina*	10 m	moderate	intolerant	green deciduous conifer	attractive bark
11. Plum Yew *Cephalotaxus drupacea*	3 m	slow	tolerant	green	dislikes extreme heat and wind
12. Torreya *Torreya nucifera*	10 m	slow	intolerant	dark green	graceful small tree with fissured bark

SPECIES	Height	Growth	Shade	Colour	Comments
13. English Yew *Taxus baccata*	10m	very slow	tolerant	dark green	unsuited to atmospheric pollution; various sub-species
14. Japanese Yew *Taxus cuspidata*	10m	slow	tolerant	dark green	several sub-species such as: *nanna, densa*
15. Ground Hemlock *Taxus canadensio*	2m	very slow	tolerant	dark green	very prostrate and hardy ground cover
16. Common Juniper *Juniperus communis*	2/3m	slow	tolerant	green	very many forms including columnor and prostrate extremes
17. Chinese Juniper *Juniperus schimonsis*	1–6m	slow	tolerant	green	very variable; can be quite large; several colour varieties
18. Red Cedar *Juniperus virginiana*	2–5m	moderate	tolerant	green	very variable in shape, form and colour
19. Cypress *Cupressus sempervivens*	10m	fast	intolerant	green	easily trimmed and kept as a bush
20. Shasta Cypress *Cupressus sempervivens*	5m	moderate	intolerant	dark green	very hardy
21. Oriental Arborvitae *Thuja orientalis*	3m	slow	tolerant	dark green	easily trimmed; several colour variations
22. Hawthorn *Crataegus monogyna*	5m	moderate	tolerant	green	very hardy and can be trimmed by pruning
23. Cockspur Thorn *Crataegus crus-galli*	5m	moderate	tolerant	green	very hardy and are suitable for pruning
24. Holly *Ilex aquifolium*	3m	moderate	tolerant	evergreen	very many varieties and colour forms
25. American Holly *Ilex opaca*	3m	moderate	tolerant	evergreen	prefers light soil with a low p.h.
26. Canadian Berberis *Berberis canadensis*	2m	moderate	tolerant	evergreen	prickly leaves; very easy to grow

SPECIES	Height	Growth	Shade	Colour	Comments
27. European Berberis *Berberis vulgaris*	2 m	moderate	tolerant	evergreen	prickly leaves; very easy to grow
28. Common Spirea *Spiraea thunbergi*	2 m	fast	tolerant	deciduous	easily grown but periodic pruning advisable
29. Laurel *Laurus noblis*	3 m	moderate	tolerant	evergreen	will grow larger in time but suited to pruning
30. Garland Flower *Daphne cneorum*	0.5 m	moderate	tolerant	evergreen	excellent ground cover
31. Spurge Laurel *Daphne laureola*	0.5 m	moderate	tolerant	evergreen	slightly more erect; ideal nesting cover
32. Everlasting Thorn *Pyracantha coccinea*	3 m	moderate	tolerant	evergreen	very beautiful and can be grown up a fence
33. Horizontal Cotoneaster *Cotoneaster horizontalis*	0.5 m	moderate	tolerant	semi-green	easily trained up fences or left prostrate
34. Rock Spray *Cotoneaster microphylla*	1 m	moderate	tolerant	evergreen	upright branching habit with dense branches
35. Scots Rose *Rosa spinosissima*	1 m	moderate	tolerant	semi-green	beautiful white flowered bush
36. Eglantine Rose *Rose eglanteria*	2 m	moderate	tolerant	semi-green	aromatic foliage, very prickly
37. Elder *Sambacus nigra*	2 m	moderate	tolerant	deciduous	easily grown
38. American Elder *Sambacus canadensis*	2 m	moderate	tolerant	deciduous	vigorous and easily grown
39. Russian Sage *Perovskia atriplicifolia*	1 m	moderate	intolerant	deciduous	beautiful and aromatic shrub
40. Golden Bell *Forsythia suspensa*	2 – 3 m	moderate	tolerant	deciduous	very attractive, free flowering species

These are just a few examples of possible aviary plants. There are obviously many more plants, including for example Lilacs, Mints, Privet, Snowberry, and all of the host of Heathers which — dependant on the birds in the enclosures — can make a very beautiful and useful addition, although being so low they are an invitation to bored or just plain curious birds. There is a further group of plants, the Rhododendrons and Azaleas; these are all very beautiful, but some species are rather rampant and cast a lot of shade. This must always be borne in mind if they are used; also there is the fact that some of them are less frost resistant, especially the Azaleas. One Rhododendron one would advise against using is the Common (or *Rhododenron ponticum*) which once established can develop very quickly into a substantial liability. Bulbs have a habit of being dug up or, if not dug up, vigorously pecked at and possibly even totally obliterated so they are not really worth pursuing. One of my special favourites is the Bramble or Blackberry which, being prickly, low growing and evergreen, is by reason of all these features indestructable and provides cover and colour all year round. I allow the birds to have the fruits out of unbridled generosity!

When purchasing plants it is invariably best to obtain container or pot grown specimens if at all possible. These plants do not go into 'check' until re-establishing new root bulbs but should grow on steadily. Where the aviary floor is built up using gravel and sand it must be remembered that this medium is very poor nutritionally, so either a small area of soil should be put in close proximity to the plant, or alternatively periodic fertilisation of the immediate area will help. This latter option may be best owing to the presence of worms which would be likely to be present in soil and their subsequent ability to act as hosts for parasitic infection if eaten by the birds, as would be highly likely.

No reference has been made to the incredibly long list of vines which can be used along aviary walls. These are so numerous and varied it would be best to establish what is available locally, always bearing in mind what you want the vine to do, assuming you need one at all of course, as some species are deciduous after a glorious riot of autumn colours. The author would not recommend any of the ivies owing to their very robust nature and later difficulties encountered if maintenance of the aviary or part of it is required, but everyone can decide for themselves of course. Ivy can be used rather well if an aviary backs on to a stone or brick wall on which it can climb.

A further factor which must not be overlooked is that of the effects on the p.h. of the soil when lime is used periodically to break down and assist in decomposition of droppings and plant litter. Obviously an acid soil specific plant will react, possibly unfavourably, to such an environment.

In conclusion, choice of suitable aviary plants leaves plenty of scope for satisfying most requirements of climate, soil, aviary height, width and depth, and the aviculturalist's personal preferences. Two of my favourites are Broom – *Cytisus sp.* of which there are so many beautiful colours in cultivation, and the Gorse – *Ulex europaeus* is the other. Both are hardy and reliable. Whatever the choice, the final arbiter is always of course what is good for the birds above all else.

Chapter 4.3

Incubation Techniques and Procedure

Having got our own choices of the Pheasant family into breeding condition we have all got to consider by what method we want to secure their incubation. Basically there are three options open for consideration, these being the Natural Mother, the Broody Hen and finally the Incubator.

Living as we do in the technological era it is a common fallacy in my view to assume that all our problems are solved in these times by the universal availability of incubators of all kinds and sizes. One can buy an incubator ranging from six Quail egg size electrically powered up to 20, 100, 500, 1000, 5000, 10,000 or more egg size, either of still air or forced air varieties. There are also the oil heated forms, and incubators which need to be hand turned or those which are automatically turned at regular intervals. With all this high flying expertise it is an amazing irony that the percentage of eggs hatched is always less than that achieved by natural incubation and so hangs many a tale either of woe or happiness.

For a number of years I have used electric incubators of varying sizes and types and have many times had to be thankful for their existence, but this in a contrary way has also served to illustrate their limitations.

Dealing with the use of electric incubators at length first, they undoubtedly have both their value and limitations. It is the understanding of their limitations which I have found most useful; this is best illustrated by my pointing an accusing finger at automatic turners. I hold to the view that if you cannot be bothered to turn your eggs yourself you are ill suited to the whole subject for two reasons; the inexplicable sheer interest, and perhaps more importantly getting to know your eggs and so knowing them that the fingers as they turn the eggs let one know instantly if an egg is either deteriorating, has stopped developing or is too dry or humid. This is not really something it is possible to teach and has to be learned from experience. Guidance and suggestions are the best which can be offered.

Basically there is the need to establish the working temperature, ideally running the machine for about a day before setting the eggs, marginal adjustments being made until the incubator settles down to a steady running temperature.

These temperatures vary according to whether or not the machine is a Convection Incubator or a Forced Air one. Another factor dictating temperature, but only marginally, is the species of eggs being incubated. In any event all eggs have a variable tolerance during their period of incubation, including cooling periods while Hen birds are off feeding and relieving themselves, at least twice a day.

For Forced Air Incubators the temperatures are set at 37.5°C (99.5°F), while Convection Incubators are set at 37.7°C (104°F). Convection Incubators are otherwise known as Still Air Incubators.

The greatest variable when operating any artificial incubator, and even with Broodies, is the humidity, and this is often poorly understood at best, but is utterly vital if any reasonable success is to be expected at all and if outright failure is to be avoided in fact. This relative humidity can range from 58–62%.

Clearly the ordinary air temperature will affect Incubators and so too will the humidity. This is expressed as ambient temperature and ambient humidity. It is most important that constant monitoring of both temperature and humidity be maintained and that the Aviculturists be familiar with the requirements for the various species with which they are working. It follows from this that it may not be possible, or at it is least inadvisable, to keep certain eggs in the same incubator owing to their differing needs.

The location of the incubators is extremely important. Apart from the need to operate a tight hygiene regime, any building which is easily influenced by outside temperatures and variable fluctuations is not suitable, as the problems of adjusting incubators to accommodate high exterior temperatures then, as the day draws to a close, guessing how far it will drop, are a nightmare. The ideal is a building which can be maintained at a reasonable constant and if possible this should be around the 22.5°C (60°F) mark.

Once we get into our incubation period, eggs, it should be remembered, slowly start to generate their own heat and this building up requires careful monitoring and adjustment of the incubator to make allowances accordingly.

When loading the larger incubators with recently laid eggs it is good practice to ensure hatching dates are at least a week apart, because during the pre-hatching period the chicks 'talk' to each other. This can make eggs due to hatch a few days later speed up, which can be disastrous for those chicks, either exhausting them before piping leading to 'dead in shell', or weak or abnormal chicks whose potential for survival is severely impaired.

Freshly laid eggs of most species have a known incubation period and by counting forward accordingly with a calendar the date of hatching can be marked, usually in pencil or felt-tipped pen, on one side of the egg and an X put on the opposite side. This serves two purposes: we firstly know when a batch of chicks might be expected; and secondly, marking eggs in this way allows us to know that we have turned every egg without missing any as either all the dates are upwards or the X's are upwards.

When dealing with eggs collected from the wild an approximate hatching date can only be guessed at; this can be entered in a form of log book and an O marked on the egg opposite to the X.

At least once a week all eggs in the incubators should be candled either with a special lamp made for that purpose (such a lamp can be easily produced by oneself using an electric light bulb and a tin can) or, as I usually use, an ordinary but fairly strong torch.

What you can expect to see is shown on Figure 9; this shows both the developing embryo and the increasing air sac. If the air sac is too small or too large the chick's development can go badly adrift in a short time. The developing embryo is a truly fascinating sight and always a wonder to me, beginning as it does around the Anus (this is known as the 'primitive streak'); then the spreading blood vessels follow rapidly. Within seven days a developing bird is becoming apparent. At this stage any candled eggs failing to show development to a similar extent, or no development, should be ruthlessly removed, and the same thing must be done at fourteen days, then as frequently thereafter as one feels necessary. It does not take

Figure 9.
Diagram of Developing Embryo

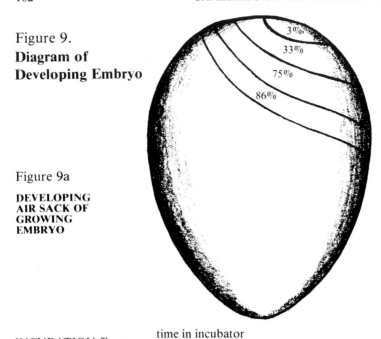

Figure 9a

DEVELOPING AIR SACK OF GROWING EMBRYO

INCUBATION % = $\dfrac{\text{time in incubator}}{\text{species incubation period}}$

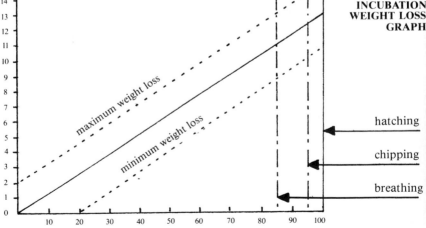

Figure 9b

INCUBATION WEIGHT LOSS GRAPH

maximum weight loss

minimum weight loss

hatching

chipping

breathing

(after Anderson Brown)

long to get the hang of the routine. Never be tempted to hang on to doubtful eggs because, especially in the confined area of an incubator, one bad egg can rapidly cross infect the others. The motto which I have pinned up as a reminder to myself is 'keep it clean – if in doubt chuck it out', and when I say out I mean right out of the building away from the incubators.

All eggs being incubated, by whatever methods, involve a weight loss in real terms. This can range from 12–15% with the best results achieved nearer the upper limit. Excepting Quail and Partridge eggs which are proportionately less, most eggs produce around 3500cc of carbon dioxide and require about 4500cc of oxygen. These gases are conducted to and from the shell which acts as a filter, through the blood vessels, where they reach the outer membrane just under the shell.

The alternatives to hatching by incubators remaining to us are either using the Broody Hen or the Natural Mother. At this point I would like to consider the Broody first. As with any option it has its advantages and disadvantages over both the Incubator and the Natural Mother.

By using the Incubator or Broody we can induce larger egg numbers to be laid and if so inclined the Natural Mother can be left with a small clutch towards the end of the season.

The advantage the Broody Hen has over the other two options is that, if it is reliable, one can achieve higher hatching percentages than obtained from Incubators and a good attentive brooder as well who is instinctively far better able to rear the chicks than would be possible under artificial brooders.

Having made use of all three systems by varying degrees in different years I have now settled down to making use of Broody Hens as much as possible. My Incubators are used as a standby or if I am given someone's unwanted surplus, and should I not have a broody suitable at that particular time. Natural hatching using the laying bird is only resorted to with late end of season clutches, owing to the high risk from disturbance of sitting birds by visitors when one is open to the visiting public. Should these birds bring off their own young, all well and good. I am naturally well pleased, but for earlier clutches I am at least assured of some success in rearing by having them under Broody Hens kept specifically for this purpose.

The use of a Broody Hen can only be successful if the Aviculturist makes a point of handling the birds frequently right from the chick stage. A tame Hen, used to one's voice, presence and handling is worth a very great deal and will more than reward the effort required to achieve this. All my Hens used for incubation have been hand reared and will readily eat from the outstretched hand as I have always made a point of encouraging them to do so.

Knowing how to pick up the birds obviously helps greatly; slow, positive and unhurried gestures are the order of the day. A quick snatch and rough handling leads to mistrust and resulting nervousness that in turn ends up in disaster at the broody stage with the birds unsettled and restless.

I always talk to my Hens and whenever time permits sit down with them while they are coming in to roost, occasionally picking one up and stroking it. This they come to accept and you soon learn each bird's character. Although perhaps to other people a few look similar they are not, and some of mine actually hop up on my lap or perch on my shoulder. This familiarity allows me to move them out of the flock and their House into a separate Brooder with no risk of upsetting them, and as an added safeguard I do this in the evening which gives them at this latitude in the spring around eight hours to get used to the Brooder before coming off to feed. I am fortunate in that most of my Hens do not even need confining to their nest box section during the initial stages which is when it becomes obvious that previous time spent befriending them pays off, as all the work needed during incubation is restricted to feeding, watering and occasional dampening of the turf to maintain humidity during incubation.

Other work entailed in this system is keeping disturbance to a minimum from Dogs, Cats, Children and even Adults, moving the Brooder Coop to fresh grass as necessary, giving extra protection from rain and wind during or in anticipation of bad weather, or providing shade when the sun is very strong – not that this happens too often in the Highlands of Scotland.

Some additional procedures which are useful as pre-emptive of future possible problems include dusting the birds with insecticide powders, initially during February, at which time the nest boxes should also be done. I repeat the process at the beginning of April, and usually avoid Birds being irritated to the point of distraction which ends up with them being liable to give up brooding.

It can be argued that incubators only cost money to run during the breeding season while a small poultry flock has to be fed all year round, which of course is very true. It also has to be argued that for at least six months of the year fresh eggs in plenty are available. I sell some of mine, and no electricity or gas bills are incurred during incubating and subsequent brooding, nor do I have to be continually in attendance checking temperatures, turning eggs and constantly worrying over the unfeathered chicks as my Hens do all this for me, with a little help of course.

One very important aspect involves choice of Poultry intended for use as potential Broody Hens. Bird size is important, but so too is weight as not all bigger breeds are heavy nor does it follow that the smaller breeds are always as light as they might seem.

Logically, the size of the egg dictates the size and weight of the breed used, and it must not be forgotten that so too does the size of the clutch intended to be put under the Hen. A fatal temptation is to put many eggs under a proven reliable Hen. She has, after all, to straddle whatever is given to her and can only heat those sides of the eggs nearest her and they must also be turned by her regularly.

For eggs of standard Poultry size I give my Fowl size breeds up to eight or nine, no more; birds of Bantam size up to five or six. Clearly smaller sized eggs can be accommodated in larger numbers, e.g. ten to twelve, and seven to nine. The number and type of eggs under each bird is clearly a matter for simple common sense, erring where necessary in favour of fewer eggs if need be. This is all the more important when dealing with small numbers of valuable eggs. Having a suitable bird recently gone broody and an appropriate clutch of eggs, the two must be brought together and this must be done ideally in a separate Brooder constructed for the purpose. I prefer to move my Broody with her own eggs first and, having satisfied myself that she is stable, very quietly and gently substitute her eggs with the intended clutch either in semi-darkness while she is sitting, or when she is off feeding. This stage is critical and requires a great deal of care and some monitoring immediately afterwards for a few hours to ensure she stays on the job, which she is almost certain to do unless something drastic occurs during or just after the switch.

It is most important that the Brooder is well designed and constructed as if mice, for example, gain access, tempted by available food, they can prove fatally unsettling to the Hen, and Rats are more than any Hen can bear. I use very small mesh over the entire floor including under the nest site, while the roof over this area is solid and weatherproof. The area above the small run section has the same size of mesh. All end sections and sides are solid wood, which has the advantage of greatly reducing draughts while also restricting visual disturbance or distractions from passing birds and, more importantly, other animals such as Cats and Dogs.

Incubation for a Hen bird, of whatever species, is an intensely and instinctively secret activity orginating as a means for survival which is still carried over in all the breeds of Domestic Hens. This need for secrecy must be considered and provided for. Whenever setting up a Brooder system, situations to avoid are excessively damp locations, exposed, windy or direct sunlight positions, and those near frequently used paths or close to children's play areas and dog kennels.

If it is located under trees or within sight of a large, mature deciduous tree, try not to forget such places are used as vantage points by Crows and Birds of Prey which, if able to see the Hen, are certainly going to be seen by her, in which case I use a Pine or Spruce branch over the top wire section. This also serves to provide shelter on hot sunny days.

Ground liable to flooding or collecting puddles after heavy rainstorms should similarly be avoided at all costs. If it is possible, there is a good chance it will happen.

Generally speaking the percentage of eggs hatched under Broody Hens is greater than that obtained from Incubators. Enough has been said of both systems for the reader to decide which one he would prefer. However, it is most unlikely that one can hatch any numbers of eggs without resorting to Incubators as a fall-back proposition.

The birds kept as a broody flock can themselves be a source of pleasure. A useful supply of eggs home-produced and known to be fresh is one factor in this; another is that of selecting and breeding offspring from your small flock suitable for exhibition. There are many poultry breeds now very rare in their own right and in need of patronage; some are not all that brilliant as layers, compared with modern computer bred strains, but they are none the less useful. One Cockerel can be satisfactorily run with four to five Hens to produce viable eggs. Although larger numbers of Hens may be kept, when eggs for hatching are needed a trio or quartet can be penned up for this purpose. If there are unsaleable or otherwise unwanted Cockerels these can always be 'freezer trained' in late Summer or early Autumn.

The Poultry breeds which I choose to keep include Scots Grey Fowls and Scots Grey Bantams, both rare breeds which quantity-wise are lousy egg layers but good Broodies. I also have a cross-bred strain bred from consistently good Broodies of various breeds, rather mongrel in ancestry but slowly evolving a 'type' of their own. As egg layers they are hopeless, but sit as tight as a drum on eggs, rocks, lumps of wood, or anything they have stuck under them, which is all I expect or want from them. Other Poultry kept are of the large Fowl type. These are excellent egg producers and the occasional one turns out to be a good Broody capable of coping with numbers of eggs of the larger size. They are really too heavy for smaller egg sizes. These birds after a few years enjoy the opportunity of providing a pleasant 'still life' surrounded by roast potatoes and fresh garden peas. There are indeed a lot of good reasons for keeping to the natural way of incubation as far as possible, having so many different bonuses.

We are now left to consider the third and final option, that of the natural Hen Pheasant, Grouse, Partridge, etc. Providing circumstances are suitable and one has assured control over the bird, its environs and all potential for disturbance, it is possible to achieve a successful hatch, but owing to the inherent nervousness of many of the species considered in this book, there is a high risk attached to incubating and rearing in this way. Few Aviculturists rely on this method to any great degree; most hedge their bets by pulling the first 5−6 eggs for artificial incubation when they do use the natural Hen, leaving her with whatever else she produces. The alternative approach is to double clutch by letting the bird set a clutch and incubate for up to seven days before removing the clutch to an Incubator or possibly a Broody. Very often most species will pause after a few days, re-commence laying, then brood their second clutch themselves.

The point of leaving the first clutch of eggs to be naturally brooded for seven days is that there is conclusive evidence to show high hatchability of eggs naturally incubated during that period when compared with those entirely incubated in an Incubator. With all our technology we may do quite well but we cannot beat Nature which, knowing Man, is probably as well.

I hope the foregoing is of some initial guide along with the accompanying illustrations. I suppose the best piece of advice for anyone learning the basics at the outset is that they would do well to apprentice themselves to one or more Aviculturists. Much can be learned this way including, of course, a few bad habits which we all have, but no amount of descriptive text can really impart the 'feel' of the subject. This has to be learned by experience.

One last point, a simple yet critical one; never turn eggs continually in the same direction round and round as this twists the internal tissues on their axis. When rolling or turning an egg for example left to right, you should then turn it right or left and, if need be when beginning, to remind yourself put in a direction arrow accordingly. As we are all left or right handed there is an instinctive urge to always turn an egg or pick something up in exactly the same way each time, so a conscious and determined effort needs to be made when having to turn eggs the opposing way. Try an experiment at any time using ordinary domestic Hen eggs and ask family or friends to do it while you watch. You will be quite surprised at how quickly they forget to go backwards on alternate turns. This problem does not occur under a Broody hen.

Incubation Period and Clutch Sizes

No.	SPECIES	Eggs	Time	Monogamous or Polygamous
1.1	Black Billed Capercaillie	5−7	27	P
1.2	Capercaillie	5−7	27	P
1.3	Black Grouse	6−10	26	P
1.4	Caucasian Black Grouse	6−8	26	P
1.5	Ptarmigan	4−7	22	M
1.6	Red Grouse	4−8	22	M
1.7	Whitetailed Ptarmigan	4−8	22	M
1.8	Willow Grouse	4−7	22	M
1.9	Canadian Spruce Grouse	5−9	21	P
1.10	Siberian Spruce Grouse	6−7	21	P
1.11	Blue Grouse	6−10	26	P
1.12	Hazel Grouse	7−11	23	M
1.13	Chinese Hazel Grouse	7−10	23	M
1.14	Ruffed Grouse	6−10	23	M/P
1.15	Greater Pinnated Grouse	10−12	24	P
1.16	Lesser Pinnated Grouse	10−12	24	P
1.17	Sharptailed Grouse	6−8	26	P
1.18	Sage Grouse	6−8	26	P
2.1	Snow Cocks	5−7	28	M
3.1/2	Pheasant Grouse	— Not Known —		
4.1	Amherst Pheasant	8−10	22	P
4.2	Golden Pheasant	8−10	22	P
4.3	White Eared Pheasant	4−7	27	M
4.4	Brown Eared Pheasant	5−8	27	M
4.5	Blue Eared Pheasant	6−8	27	M
4.6	Caucasian Pheasant	10−15	23	P

Incubation Period and Clutch Sizes *(continued)*

No.	SPECIES	Eggs	Time	Monogamous or Polygamous
4.7	Green Pheasant	8−12	23	P
4.8	Copper Pheasant	6−12	24	P
4.9	Reeves Pheasant	7−14	25	P
4.10	Mikado Pheasant	5−10	27	P
4.11	Elliots Pheasant	6−8	25	P
4.12	Himalayan Monal	4−8	28	M
4.13	Chinese Monal	4−8	28	M
4.14	Sclater's Monal	4−8	28	M
5.1	See-see Partridge	5−6	23	M
5.2	Sand Partridge	4−6	23	M
5.3	Barbary Partridge	8−12	24	M
5.4	Rock Partridge	7−10	24	M
5.5	Red Legged Partridge	9−14	24	M
5.6	Black Francolin	6−10	23	M
5.7	Common Partridge	8−12	26	M
6.1	Bobwhite Quail	10−14	23	M
6.2	Common Quail	10−12	18	M
6.3	Californian Quail	10−12	22	M
6.4	Gambel's Quail	10−16	23	M
6.5	Scaled Quail	10−14	23	M
6.6	Montezuma Quail	6−14	26	M
6.7	Mountain Quail	7−10	28	M
7.1	Turkey	15−20	28	P

EGG PRODUCTION, COLLECTION AND STORAGE

Egg production, of course, is what it is all about. In one sense it is the culmination of a year's work in breeding the birds up to their reproductive peak. Looked at another way it could be thought of as the start of another year, and that is the way, rightly or wrongly, in which I see it.

Work does not start when the first egg is laid, as that would find all of us in a corner. I start thinking about the arrival of the first egg in January by going over all my equipment, especially for incubation, which is all dealt with under a separate chapter. Here I will start with storage trays as the first step associated with egg collection and storage.

Large scale producers of Pheasants for shooting purposes cannot afford the time needed, by reason of sheer volume, for individual attention to each egg and will accept the penalty of lower hatchability percentages. Aviculturists invariably regard each egg as a future chick, or at least secretly hope each egg can be converted into a chick, that chick to a poult and that poult to an adult. It never happens quite that way, not ever, but it does not make the slightest difference as each year we still entertain our high expections.

The old saying of "never count your chickens until they hatch" must have been thought up a very long time ago, more than likely by a simple and wise old fellow, and it is as true now as it ever was. One thing is for sure: if one's birds have the good grace to go to the trouble of laying a good fertile egg for us the least we can do is make sure its path to hatching is as trouble-free and as smooth as possible, quite literally.

Having got our first egg, what do we do with it? Obviously it would be silly and also quite wrong to put each egg in the incubator, mechanical or feathered, as it is laid, so we must devise a safe, secure place for them which has a satisfactory environment with regard mainly to humidity and temperature.

There are three principle methods commonly used in Aviculture, or versions of the same. First the papier-mâché egg trays for domestic poultry can be used, placing the eggs with their points downward; secondly, an angled tray divided vertically with runners and horizontally with dowels in which eggs are laid on their sides by points slightly downward can be used; thirdly, a metal or wooden tray with a layer of clean fine sand in it on which the eggs can be laid again sideways with the points slightly downward.

I have tried all three and disliked the first most as it consistently could be shown statistically to produce the poorest results. The second system is quite widely used and never questioned but I have very great doubts about the wisdom of this method. It does undeniably make turning of eggs quite a bit easier, but I think at the cost of unnecessary strain to the egg's shell, a factor never encountered in nature. I will admit it is a small point but it could affect the hatchability of eggs by a few percentage points or make a weak chick's chances of survival all but impossible.

The third method has served me well and in the absence of a better alternative I propose staying with the sand tray. The positive advantages I have found include the cradling or moulding effect the sand has to the shape of the eggs. It is naturally a fairly sterile environment and can be easily fumigated to maintain an infection-free medium. There is another big bonus, which is the ease with which the eggs can be mist-sprayed with water during periods of high temperature and the attendant low humidity that goes with such weather.

Regardless of method, I would suggest all eggs are stored in a darkened room or cupboard, failing which a thick hessian sack carefully draped over the eggs will greatly help, especially if they are kept well away from the magnifying effect on heat from the window. Ideal storage temperatures and humidity are 13°C (55°F) and 75–80% respectively.

Temperature fluctuations for eggs in storage should be reduced as much as possible from the outset. A narrow range of variation will not cause any undue problems as the eggs are naturally designed to

Figure 10. **Diagram of Trays**

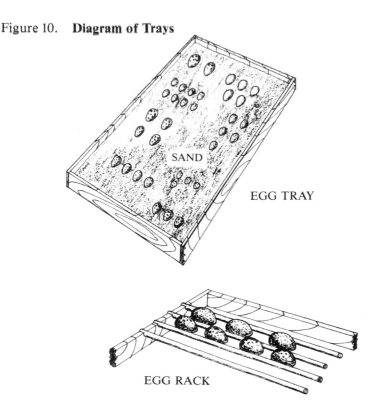

SAND

EGG TRAY

EGG RACK

cope with some variations of both temperature and humidity, both of which are important, the latter equally so though this is often overlooked or ignored. It is worth remembering that while a clutch is being laid it is subject to the effects of dew and often rain, so too dry is worse than too wet.

At the risk of appearing to labour a point this business of storage, humidity and temperature is utterly vital to hatching percentages. It is no good glibly quoting figures; for each species in nature there is variable success, and each species has its optimum needs for humidity and temperature. I can only urge readers to consider the likely requirements for each of their species. If a species comes from a relatively arid area its needs are bound to be different from those of a species from a wet, temperate area and we ought not to lose sight of this important point. When deciding to collect eggs from Aviary birds certain points must be considered such as: do we want the Hen to do her own incubation? If we do then she should be left alone. Another option is to let her lay around 8–10 eggs then remove these for incubation, leaving her to deal with the second clutch herself, if she can reasonably be expected to do so under her Aviary conditions.

With rare species naturally laying small clutches, it may be prudent to 'pull' the eggs as they are laid; storing beyond seven days is to be avoided and deterioration beyond 10 days is quite noticeable.

This 'pulling' of eggs is a very effective management tool used wisely, and can significantly raise production, especially if there is any likelihood of early eggs being infertile. I tried an experiment with a Hen Caucasian Pheasant who would not brood, although her mother in the same Aviary went down every time. For two consecutive seasons this lady produced 86 eggs in her first year and 97 in her second year. In both years she laid double-yoked eggs and signed off her second season with an egg the size of a thumb nail and quite yokeless. Many of her eggs hatched, but eventually I had to empty them and feed the contents to the dogs as all the incubators had to be shut off for the season when fertility dropped off. I came to two conclusions; the first was to release her as she had earned her ticket if ever anyone did; the second was never to let dogs eat raw eggs as the atmosphere changed markedly as it would do with any dog, but imagine the situation when you try it on three Wolfhounds. I learn from my mistakes in time!

So far we have been concerned with eggs produced from captive birds, but it is very important to look at the collection of eggs from the wild. This often takes place, particularly to broaden genetic material where numbers of a species in captivity are low and in-breeding becomes either a risk or an actual impediment to sustaining captive populations.

Legislation concerning collections from the wild varies according to country and may involve only local permission from the land-owner or right through to Government permits or licences.

Assuming that one may properly take the eggs there are two methods: either watching and searching over known breeding habitats on foot, or also on foot but in company with a pointing breed of dog. Given the required patience, the first method I have found to be easy when using binoculars in searching for the *Lagopus* group of Grouse, as the Cocks eventually show themselves on a prominent part of their territory and somewhere in the surrounding 2–10 hectares the Hen will be sitting.

When looking for forest dwelling species or those on forest margins a dog will take the luck out of searching, reduce wasted time and minimise disturbance to other wildlife, but only a properly trained dog should be used out of concern for other species and the effect an uncontrollable dog may have on the landowners' other interests.

Transportation from nest to Incubator or Broody Hen is the next hurdle and at all costs care must be taken to avoid shaking the embryos within or cracking the eggs. I use polystyrene egg boxes for short trips, held shut by a rubber band and then placed in a back pack. For trips involving more than an hour the eggs are packed in eiderdown, collected for that purpose, and carefully spaced in a large container; this is a very effective means of avoiding vibration and conserving heat loss. I have heard of the use of a wide-mouthed Thermos Flask filled with heated grain but I also know that this has produced overheated eggs and I rather think risk of breakage is too high. If I had gone high up into the mountains to collect Ptarmigan and got back with eggs unhatchable for whatever reason then I would be greatly annoyed at wasting both the eggs and my time and effort.

At the risk of stating the obvious, it is essential to get the eggs under heat without delay. The eggs can be candled after 24–48 hours when they have had time to stabilise. Each clutch, if there are more than one, should be marked by a felt-tipped pen to distinguish be-tween them and also to facilitate their proper turning if an incubator is to be used.

Chapter 4.4

Rearing and Feeding

REARING TECHNIQUES AND PROCEDURE

Hopefully, having hatched one's eggs satisfactorily, the major difficulty remaining to be overcome is getting the Chicks through the Poult stage and into an over-wintering condition.

Exactly how this is achieved is partly dictated by the method used in incubation, at least as far as Brooding is concerned, and it is with Natural Brooding that I would like to begin.

As can be expected, the privacy needed by an incubating bird should continue to be available, especially during the period immediately post-hatching. This avoids needless stress for the parent, or foster parent, which should be gradually accustomed to strange sights and sounds because total seclusion forever is impossible.

For birds of all ages sudden noises and movements are stressful and should always be avoided, but equally important is the need to gradually accustom and condition birds first of all to their attendant – be it oneself or another member of the family. One of the best ways to achieve this is to whistle repetitively or call softly in a way with which the birds can become familiar. Birds will more readily accept sounds than movement, and this should be borne in mind by all Aviculturists.

During this early stage in the Chick's life two rather important considerations other than food are protection from draughts and damp. It is very important to develop some skill at anticipating deterioration in the weather so that a suitable covering may be put over the outer run and the birds shut in at night. Limited access out to feed and exercise may well be needed in exceptionally bad weather. This should be done under supervision and if the chicks look fluffed up and hunched then they should be encouraged to take shelter with the Hen then allowed out again later for further food and exercise.

I prefer to keep the Hen with her chicks in the smaller coops during the initial 2−3 weeks, moving the coop on to fresh grass as required. Diet at this stage is most important and should have a great deal of time, thought and effort applied to it, ensuring the freshness of all components including as much as anything the water, which should be changed frequently. Water can very easily become stale through contamination from food on the birds' bill and dirt from their feet.

After the three week stage young birds with their foster Hen can then be moved into a larger, moveable pen and the same procedure followed, but an overnight shelter or coop needs to be incorporated along with Spruce or Pine branches for shelter in various suitable places. An additional protection can be the clear corrugated perspex which can be put in as a roof across one end at the same height as the solid side panels.

After the first six weeks the foster Hen can be removed, leaving the young birds by themselves but, dependent on species, if there is insufficient room for the birds there may be the possibility of feather pecking at any age. This must be guarded against and stopped by splitting up the birds beforehand, especially amongst those species known to be pugnacious, otherwise the situation could well develop into fatalities.

While Brooding with a foster Hen is comparatively simple and inexpensive the same cannot be said of Artificial Brooding, either by use of Electricity of Bottled Gas. Quite apart from the cost of these energy sources and the equipment and housing associated with this method, there is also the considerable time required in operating these sytems and they can go wrong through technical failures.

When rearing large numbers of birds artificial brooding has very many favourable aspects. The labour, heat and other costs are fixed and once set up are the same whether one puts 10, 100 or 200 Chicks inside, dependent obviously on house size. The standard 2.40×1.20 m house is designed to take 200 Caucasian Pheasant size day-old Chicks.

These Brooder Houses are constructed in sections using marine or exterior grade ply. They are fairly easily moved and can be located

Figure 11.   **Brooder Layout and Siting**

Figure A

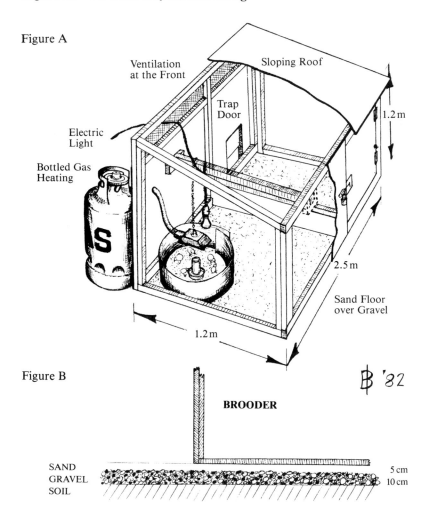

Ventilation at the Front

Sloping Roof

Trap Door

1.2 m

Electric Light

Bottled Gas Heating

S

2.5 m

Sand Floor over Gravel

1.2 m

Figure B

₿ '82

BROODER

SAND
GRAVEL
SOIL

5 cm
10 cm

each year on fresh ground. The foundations should be prepared beforehand using gravel for a base with a reasonable depth of sand on top. This preparatory work is of great importance, ensuring not only good drainage but a fairly sterile environment, thus reducing the likelihood of worms and other invertibrates which might act as a host or vector for infections that might be ingested through eating anything contaminated, and which would be readily available and attractive to Chicks and growing Poults.

When the Brooder House has been set up firmly on a good base a sectional Pen can be erected on the side of the House in which a hatch is located. The interior of the Brooder House has a central division with which to isolate one half, in which the young Chicks are maintained under their heater lamp during their first week. Ideally the corners should be blocked, or a ring of cardboard placed directly under the lamp, which can be slowly widened as the Chicks develop and can be conditioned to their heat source. As time passes and further room is needed by the rapidly growing birds, the central division can be removed and whenever, weather permits, access to the grassed area of the sectional pen can be permitted for short periods under careful supervision initially.

This access to the outside pen becomes an important feature in the birds' welfare and good steady growth, allowing as it does ample exercise and natural insect life as a supplement to their diet, as is the grass. The grass initially must be very short, to avoid chilling resulting from walking through damp long grass.

For up to about six weeks it is advisable to shut the birds in each night; they very soon learn if a routine is followed and will often head for home of their own accord. There are always a few laggards who could get caught out in night time rain.

As the birds increase in size and are more mobile, perches should be provided at varying heights, in different places. Most species, including young Quail, will take advantage of these perches which will serve them well in the future and keep them off the damp and out of ground level draughts, which can make a substantial difference to the incidence of illness or death during severe weather by having the birds out of the way of these problems. One further advantage is that droppings under roosting perches are concentrated in specific places from which they can be conveniently removed, limiting to some degree the risk of contamination in feeding, gritting and dusting areas.

Clearly most of what has been said applies to the large species, but insofar as Quail are concerned adaptations in terms of scale are easily worked out. There is the extra problem of controlling the diminutive Chicks and a little hole or gap is a potential escape route. Once out they almost never find their own way back in and speedily become victims, if not to predation, by being trodden on or simply from cold.

Naturally any hole through which a Quail Chick can escape is an entrance for Mice, small Rats and even Weasels, none of which are noted for improving a Chick's health.

Diet at the rearing stage is vital, for birds ranging from the humble little Quail right through to the magnificent large Capercaillie, and all sizes in between. During a chick's earliest weeks its body's sole objective is to increase as fast as possible, at least until they can get on the wing. It is both difficult and important to maintain the availability and varying proportions of protein, vitamins, energy and calcium. A useful source these days is the proprietory foods in Crumb or Pellet form which are manufactured specifically to suit Caucasian Pheasants reared for shooting. This food is principally suited for all the Pheasants and Partridges. For the Grouse, however, it is more appropriate to use Turkey feed as the composition is different and better. This leaves us with the Quails, which can certainly use the Chick starter crumbs but need other additions such as Millet and Canary seed.

For all species ready access should be given to grass where possible and valuable benefits can be had from providing Chickweed, chopped Lettuce and Spinach. I grow everlasting Spinach and Lettuce specifically for feeding to my young birds. Dandelion is another good food chopped up. However, it is not a useful proposition for me as it hardly is to be found in this mountainous part of Scotland. Most readers will not have this problem, but it is important to avoid collecting leaves from areas likely to be subject to contamination such as from lead on roadsides or chemicals used in spraying, and nowadays there are very few areas where this can be the case in Western Europe or North America.

One very important aspect in providing adequate resources for Gamebirds is an adequate and reliable supply of Grit. Each species has its varying requirements, but if a regular availability is ensured each bird may regulate its own requirements. This Grit should be of a hard type and provided in a separate receptacle where it is unlikely to be contaminated by droppings or stale water.

Some Aviculturists make use of hard-boiled and chopped eggs as a source of protein for very young birds. This is in theory a good food, but during very hot weather it deteriorates rapidly with attendant risks of scouring which, if serious, can cause the death of any Chick finding a previously overlooked crumb that may have lain for some time.

Mealworms are also used, but one well known Aviculturist, Dr. Aschenbrenner in Germany, told me he no longer uses Mealworms as Chicks and Poults in his experience sometimes develop the habit of pecking their own and siblings' toes which look somewhat similar, with the resulting discomfort, lameness and infections that can occur.

Whatever food is provided it is as well to feed in small quantities but often. This maintains the certainty of fresh food at all times, maintaining palatability, and keeps the birds actively moving, searching and interested. One positive benefit in another direction is to reduce aggression and feather pecking amongst otherwise bored birds kept in groups, large or small.

It is essential during the rearing process to keep the birds active and interested. One useful means towards this end is to hang a bunch of vegetation suitable as a food supplement, such as seeded grasses, heather, willow, hazel and conifer branches, at a height requiring the birds to jump and peck.

One of the great advantages in keeping birds where possible and practical on a naturally grassed area is that there is an excellent food resource in the form of insects and invertibrates which they can search for and eat, thus making for a valuable contribution in their diet while occupying the birds and exercising them. This cannot happen with birds kept on wire and there is an ever present risk of unfit, overweight and lethargic birds which must be less able to relate normally to one another with all that this implies.

In concluding this Chapter mention should be made of the equipment available for artificial brooding, in particular the heat sources. Bottled Propane Gas is widely used and has the advantage of maintaining reasonable levels of humidity while warming the Chicks. It is a prudent measure to operate bottles in pairs with an automatic switch-over device which cuts in when one of the bottles runs out. Propane Gas also emits a dull glow that attracts the Chicks to the heat source when they might otherwise huddle into corners away from observable heat resulting in smothering and chilling. The actual heater is suspended on a chain that can be raised or lowered in relation to bird height and temperature, which can slowly be decreased as the birds feather up and are hardened off. One such heater can cope with up to 200 birds if positioned properly in a suitable house.

Where electricity is the preferred or available heat source for brooding this is generally done by using infra-red lamps, which can similarly be raised and lowered according to the birds' requirements.

The light source attracts the birds and avoids the problems mentioned above. A good indication of the relative comfort of the birds can be had by noting if they are tightly packed underneath the lamp, in which case the heat is insufficient and the bulb should be lowered. Conversely, if the birds are well scattered, leaving a vacant place beneath the bulb, then it should be raised. In both cases outside temperatures vary according to the weather and the lamp or heater will need to be raised or lowered accordingly.

Another form of electric lamp is the *Salamander Dull Emiter* which provides heat without any form of light. Whereas the above infra-red lamps operate on short wave, the Dull Emiters operate on medium wave using a ceramic bulb which, unlike the above, will not shatter if splashed by water. This form of medium wave heating is relatively new, but while it has proved itself satisfactory and superior in many ways it is not widely used yet, perhaps partly due to a lack of understanding of the principles of operation and partly because the actual heat is not visual in any form, as some 96% of energy used is converted to heat. Bulb life is around ten times greater than for short wave, 1000 to 10,000 hours respectively. Unlike the short wave heat, that from medium wave does not affect the vitamin element in feed.

The effect of medium wave heat is confined to the heat pores just below skin level. Viscosity of the blood is slightly reduced, thereby increasing blood circulation and the metabolic rate of the birds.

Perhaps the major benefit to be had from using this type of lamp is that regardless of the crossflow of air, the heat produced is not dissipated. This is a significant advance as it permits the provision of a heat source for birds in outdoor aviaries, either by providing energy fields covering under, for example, a roofed-over section only or the entire Aviary, however large, if that is what is required.

It is interesting to note the length of electricity units compared to the size of lamp; one 150 watt bulb will operate for seven hours on one unit while one 250 watt bulb will operate for four hours.

Both forms of infra-red heating appropriate for birds have as their major drawback the problem of what to do during a power failure and some sort of provision ought to be made to cover for such an eventuality. Obviously it goes without saying that if you take such precautions as like as not they are never needed but when you do not they are!

In conclusion, for anyone ever stuck with no room in existing brooders when an unexpected brood of anything turns up at short notice, I have been able to get myself out of trouble on more than one occasion by using a 'Heath Robinson' affair involving a domestic table lamp painted red with one of my daughter's water colours. This, combined with a cardboard box, worked satisfactorily. I also used the same size of bulb (60 watt) fitted to a light fitting and screwed into an old tomato box which in turn was turned upside down with the bulb suspended over another box 50cm deep. In both cases these apparently crazy setups were able to rear several clutches of Gamebirds, Poultry and even Ducklings – without loss, something I cannot claim for custom manufactured Brooders.

In simple terms, provided adequate heat, water and food are available along with a little ingenuity and time, anybody can make a brooder cheaply and produce satisfactory results. Necessity is most certainly the mother of invention and high technology does not always rule, especially when funds are a little short.

NUTRITION AND FEEDING

Very extensive studies at the Grouse Research Unit in Scotland, both in captivity and in the field, have shown that quality of food directly affects the success of the offspring of the birds eating that food. It must logically follow that this would hold true for all other Gallinaceous birds, and in fact all types of birds.

The quality of the nutritional requirements for any given species is not necessarily the same for, or even acceptable to, another species. It is therefore a very early pre-requisite to establish the best diet required by each species one proposes to keep, and determine whether such a diet can be reliably and regularly available.

A great deal of work has been undertaken on diets for certain species of those birds covered by this book, but just as many, if not more, have not received any investigation and before proceeding further it must be said that in no possible way could the ground covered by this book on this subject be in any way definitive. Basically Gamebird nutrition is still to be fully explored, and for that matter so has Human nutrition.

What can be said perhaps is that some basic guide lines are now apparent. We know the vegetarians and the seed eaters, the insectivores and those who have varying proportions of these requirements. For some species there are seasonal requirements and, if anything, this is perhaps the most important aspect of diet, especially for Hens prior to breeding, followed by that needed by Chicks in their first few weeks of life.

Regardless of what a species' diet is composed of, the freshness of food is fairly critical. The problems associated with stale or potentially contaminated food are legion and lead to the cause of the highest percentages of mortality, directly or indirectly, among birds in captivity.

When considering a species' dietary requirements in captivity, it is important to know something of their foraging behaviour in the wild. This will reveal seasonal variations, if there are any, either by origin or quantity. By knowing these two factors some reasonable estimate may be possible for food value.

There is as great a variety of food origin/type as there are Pheasants and Grouse to eat them, but practicalities prevent a faithful copying in all respects, all of the time, or even some of the time, so we must try to produce the best alternative.

In the case of the True Pheasants there are few problems left to overcome, but the same cannot be said for many of the other species covered by the range of this book. We know of the needs of the True Pheasants, Grey Partridge and the Red Legged Partridge, and now suitable pelleted proprietory foods are available from the cradle to the grave and medicated before they are packed and despatched. End of challenge, or is it?

I think no-one would deny that the availability of foods in such a form is highly convenient, but for those Aviculturists interested in the long-term welfare − particularly of the less common species in captivity, and especially of the rare and endangered − consideration ought to be given to the long-term effect of the selection pressures on such species from this and other directions. What particularly concerns myself and others is the risks inherent in blanket medication throughout a breeding bird's life.

Considering this medication procedure through the pelleted feed in depth we first come abruptly up against a dilemma of monumental proportions. All of us are aware that in their natural state species can be subject to mortality up to and exceeding 50% quite easily, partly due to predation of course, but also as a result of disease, which is one of the selection pressures all species must face. Take this away and one unquestionably both weakens the genetic material and starts along the path to domestication.

At this point I suspect if some readers have not already skipped along to another chapter they may feel inclined to do so, but I hope they will bear with me.

If we reduce a species' ability to survive naturally while in captivity, the prospects for their survival, if being produced for re-introduction, is reduced and then their ability to become established is highly questionable. If that happens, what precisely is the role of the Aviculturist?

The difficulty is knowing how far along that road we must travel, because while security in some respects is enhanced in captivity, so too are the risks from so many infections and the increased incidence of infections. We therefore cannot entirely ignore these difficulties or bird losses would become unbearable; so some form of medication is necessary.

As mentioned above, many pelleted preparations have medication incorporated at the point of manufacture, but water soluble treatments are also available and their periodic use three or four times a year is very beneficial.

Personally, I try to maintain as closely as possible a natural diet, particularly during what is loosely termed the 'maintenance' period. For birds to be brought into breeding condition I work out the diet changeover from the maintenance diet to the full breeders ration in the proprietory pelleted form during January. This is done by slowly altering the ratio of pellets in the feed throughout a five week period, climbing by one-fifth each week.

Beginning this early in the year may seem like a needless luxury, but I believe it is more than justified and I still, on an irregular basis, supplement this pelleted food by adding elements of a natural food source or sources.

Where available, I think the use of a proprietory feed for chicks and poults is really advisable. Trying to maintain a natural diet during this period for such young birds is not warranted, owing to the attendant risk of mortality at this age. It is vital to ensure the protein supply, and its freshness during this stage. I get very dispirited losing any chicks, particularly during the first 6–8 weeks, as I really do enjoy hatching and rearing young birds. As the season runs down I just grab anything to rear, including domestic poultry. Once my birds have fledged I very slowly modify the proprietory pellet diet, commencing with natural titbits, enabling the birds to explore alternative foods before having to rely on them to any great extent.

I cannot over emphasise this slow exploration-adjustment period too much. It is very important, in my opinion. If the youngsters are not properly set up for winter they may well not get through it. Even if attempts are made to redress the shortfall 'there seems to be a clear metabolic difference in need and conversion which, when it changes around the 12 week stage, has been irretrievably lost and the birds are severely disadvantaged.

This mixture of Natural Foods and proprietory pellets seems a reasonably sound compromise which allows the birds some opportunities to acquire natural resistances which they need. It may be that a few birds might be lost, but anything below 50% mortality rate is ahead of nature and allows inherently weak birds to be naturally culled out of the flock, thereby maintaining vigour within the Aviaries.

The subject of a natural diet, or a diet supplemented by natural foods, is rather vexed. Before we can provide it we must be aware of what the diet consists of, then how available or accessible the components are, and finally what cost in terms of time and labour is associated with collection as well as provision. In this regard I am rather more fortunate than others. Preferring the Grouse as I do, and living in 'Grouse Country', limitless supplies are available at no cost other than that of transport and my own time.

The form and content of Gamebird nutrition includes obviously Protein, Vitamins, Fibre and one of the means by which it is made available, grit. In the wild, according to needs the birds know what, where, when and by how much, but captivity restricts this foraging opportunity so Aviculturists, according to species kept, must by varying degrees of effort strive to make careful assessments and provision. If for some reason there is any doubt about availability and reliability, it is not ethical in my view to attempt to keep such birds whatever they are, if all that lies in store is an endless series of pellets, pellets and more pellets.

Whatever food is provided for a bird's diet, it is worth stating that the volume of food consumed is related to its energy value but this is not necessarily so in relation to protein. Should an imbalance occur between energy and protein then although the birds may not be hungry their physical welfare will deteriorate; so in preparing

a natural diet all values of component foods must be considered and
this can vary where vegetable matter is concerned according to the
quality of the soil on which this material grew. Examples of approximate values are given below:—

Description	Digestible Protein %	Energy: K cals/kg	Vitamins: A.D3.E	Minerals: Iron and Calcium
Apple	0.3	94.50	Low	Low
Banana	1.1	152.22	High	Low
Orange	0.8	71.85	Low	Low
Sultanas	1.7	512.29	Low	High
Cabbage	1.5	249.00	High	High
Lettuce	1.1	22.72	High	High
Potato	8.3	600.00	Low	High
Spinach	2.7	45.00	High	High
Alfalfa-Lucerne	12.3	227.22	High	High
Beef	14.8	640.00	Low	Low
Egg	11.9	325.00	High	High
Insects	45.0	—	—	—
Insect Larvae	45.0	—	—	—
Barley	11.3	550.00	—	—
Wheat	10.5	600.00	—	—
Oats	10.0	545.45	—	—
Maize	9.0	654.54	—	—
Starter (Turkey)	26.0	681.00	—	—
Rearer (do.)	23.0	648.00	—	—
Grower (do.)	18.0	648.00	—	—
Breeder (do.)	18.0	600.00	—	—

Adapted from R. D. Murray (1977).

Chapter 4.5
Artificial Propagation of Gamebirds for Hunting

In this chapter the range of species being considered is limited to the True Pheasants, Partridges *(Alectoris)*, Common Partridge and some North American Quail species.

Both private and commercial shooting interests are nowadays seeking and expecting large numbers of birds to be available for hunters in Europe, North America and Japan. These demands are today well in excess of demands earlier in this century owing to larger numbers of individuals with social mobility and higher disposable incomes. The natural reproductive ability of all species has been greatly exceeded by the hunting demands made of them which now requires increasing reliance on artificial propagation by Gamebird Farms specifically set up for this purpose in conjunction with efforts by sporting syndicates, landowners and other individuals.

It is a general rule that for any given number of birds released some 50% is the maximum which can be harvested by shooting. Of the remainder a proportion, which will vary according to circumstances, are removed by predators both avian and mammalian, some by disease and accidents. In total this extra loss may be some 25 – 30%.

Any given area of habitat has its optimum carrying capacity for all species of flora and fauna. In the case of the Gamebirds being considered these habitats, if occupied, range from Poor to Rich and will accordingly reflect the numbers sustainable on them.

Other factors, which are barely the same each year, include such unpredictable aspects as Weather, Crop and Fruit availability, intensity of Natural Predation and so forth. In any event, as a general rule, in a normal self sustaining population, rarely does more than 50% of any population survive the first winter and not all of the survivors will in fact breed in the following spring.

Figure 12.   **Artificial Propagation of Gamebirds for Hunting**

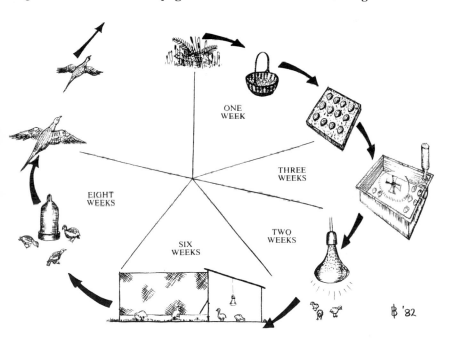

The morality of producing large quantities of birds to shoot like so much Poultry is not a matter for this book, more for the individual conscience; even so there must be a distinction between the manner in which some birds are reared and released in comparison with others. I have seen wilder Domestic Hens than some of the Pheasants that are put up for shooting.

If shooting of Gamebirds is to continue, and there can be absolutely no doubt that it will, there are obvious benefits for any given species of bird in having numbers propagated and released thereby ensuring the survival of the species on the one hand and the preservation of that species' Habitat on the other. It is something of an anachronism that where any species assumes an economic value to Man its conservation and future is reasonably assured.

One would be ill advised to assume too high a mind on this matter for as a result of the basic knowledge developed for propagating Gamebirds to be hunted modern Aviculturists now have well tried methods and techniques which make their interests and those of Conservationists possible and practical. Perhaps it would not be stretching the point to suggest that if this knowledge was not so very readily available species like the Cheer, Humes, Elliots and others might not just be unavailable in Aviculture but greatly endangered if not even exterminated.

The principles associated with artificial propagation for release are basically similar; only the methods vary according to whether one is working with the True Pheasants – *Colchicus* species, Partridges and Quail. While it is not my intention to deal in any great detail with this aspect I hope the following outline may be a useful general guide, dealing as it does with each family.

TRUE PHEASANTS

The species referred to are the Caucasian Pheasant, Japanese Green Pheasant and the Copper Pheasant, being in that order the three species generally propagated for Hunting. Clearly the Caucasian – *Colchicus colchicus* super species is by far the most commonly propagated of all Pheasants and is, in fact, well in excess of all other Gamebirds put together. Many of the sub-species/races are hopelessly intermixed and this species is now well down the road to domestication with frequent cases of abnormal specimens and several mutations including Melanistic, Flavistic, Albino and true White strains as with the Domestic Fowl.

In commencing propagation, if there is not a small nucleus of a captive flock which is maintained in pens the more usual method of catching up breeding birds is adopted. This catching up is invariably done in either late January or February with a preponderance of Hens to Cocks something of the order of 1:5 to 1:7. A higher ratio of Hens to Cocks leads to a drastic loss in fertility of those eggs gathered up.

Having caught up the required number of birds, which are then moved into large Breeding Pens, usually located either in an open area of Scrubby Forest or an overgrown field or somewhere similar, it is essential to provide sufficient cover in which birds can both roost and lay eggs without disturbance or loss. Ideally these eggs should be collected at least twice a day, if not more often as, being bored, some of the birds, Cocks or Hens, could begin egg eating, which once started rapidly spreads amongst the flock.

Care will have to be taken to ensure that safeguards are made to prevent predation on both the eggs and the birds by either birds or animals. This can be done by netting over the area or by more direct methods. Whether the area is netted over or not it is advisable to feather-clip one wing of each bird to prevent both escape or panic flights which might result in damage or death. These feathers regrow during the summer moult enabling the birds to resume full flight by the Autumn, ahead of the hunting season.

Until the end of February, a maintenance diet is quite adequate if liberally supplied, while during March a gradual changeover to a Breeder's diet can be instigated. An early flush of eggs can be more of a nuisance than an advantage, putting a strain on both the birds, their fertility and their keeper's time and energies.

Onset of natural laying varies according to the latitude and hence the photo period, and to a lesser extent the weather. For example, young Pheasants can be first hatching in Southern England or France before they have even started laying in Scotland or Scandinavia. It is well worth administering anti-gapes medication either through the drinking water or feed at monthly intervals while birds are penned up. In my view it is not sound practice to medicate in a blanket fashion as this can lead to problems eventually by reducing the bird's resistance when they are eventually released after laying.

Egg collection from the birds each day continues until either the numbers of eggs needed have been collected and set or until egg production falls off. There are two additional ways of boosting production. the first is to pick up a clutch or clutches from nests found in the wild. As long as this is done early enough during incubation the Hen Pheasants will re-cycle and produce a replacement clutch. With the second method, having obtained sufficient eggs for incubation, the birds can then be released and will almost certainly produce and rear a clutch of their own, albeit a late one.

For those who only aspire to a small or modest increase in numbers in the immediate area around them and have, or have access to, either a few broody Bantams or small Incubators, it would be a good idea to collect a few wild clutches and rear them, always assuming the necessary permission is available, which may or may not be required. Although I do not shoot myself I do release a few birds because it seems like a good idea and it gives me a lot of interest and pleasure.

Having hatched the eggs collected, the birds are then transferred to Brooder houses which are usually built to house 100 to 200 chicks in batches. These Brooders are sometimes heated electrically but more often, because the houses are transferred to different sites each year, the most convenient method to use is Propane Gas bottles.

The site for the Brooder houses should be chosen carefully. It must offer adequate shelter and be on well drained soils, in a draught-free position, ideally on a good grass turf. Under the actual brooder a layer of gravel and good course sand should be spread as an additional precaution against damp; this also facilitates good foot growth, breakdown of droppings and reduces risk of disease.

These Brooders are vital to the young birds' welfare, especially during the first six weeks of their life; during good weather the birds can eventually be allowed outside for a few hours at a time but are best locked inside at the slightest suggestion of rain – a 10 minute shower can prove fatal. In such large numbers, under confined conditions boredom can lead to feather picking and biting, both of which can be overcome by fitting small bits passed through either side of the nostrils on the upper mandible, a process which does not involve mutilation or pain, and which can be easily removed when the birds are released.

When the Pheasants are judged to be hardy enough to leave the Brooders and their runs they are then transferred to the release pens which are located in the areas in which they will be expected to establish themselves.

It is important to be constantly vigilant as far as predators are concerned; according to local legislation certain mammals may or may not be protected, so methods to prevent damage will have to be adopted accordingly. Birds of Prey, both nocturnal and diurnal, are now, however, universally protected which means that while in pens the Pheasant moults must be netted over and some means adopted to discourage perching nearby as panicking birds can easily injure or kill themselves as a consequence.

After release it is necessary to continue feeding for some time; this has the advantages of preventing straying, allowing for a period of adjustment to natural foraging and monitoring numbers as well as health while the birds reach maturity.

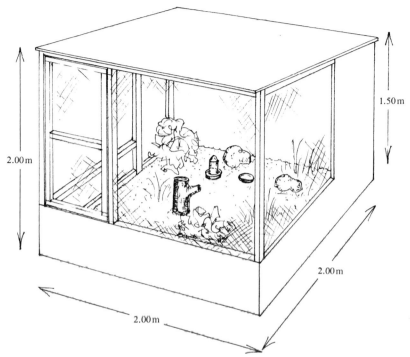

Figure 13.   **Laying Pen for Partridges**

PARTRIDGES

There are really three species covered here: the first is the Common
or Grey Partridge, the second the Red Legged or French Partridge,
and the third the Rock Partridge of which a commonly used sub-
species is the Chukar Partridge.

Owing to highly intensive agricultural practice at this time involving what can only be described as saturation herbicides, fungicides
and pesticides, the natural insect-life foods for Partridge chicks
especially are severely restricted, as too are the sheltered hedges and
field sides, so numbers of Partridges are only available now when
considerable effort is devoted to their captive propagation.

Unlike the polygamous Pheasant, Partridges, being Monogamous,
need to be housed as pairs in pens that are rather capital intensive,
as is the labour associated with their management. Eggs, if 'pulled'

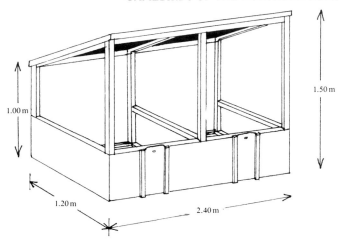

Figure 14.   **Laying Pen for Quail**

as they are laid, can be produced in quite high numbers but not as
high as with Pheasants. After transferring the eggs to incubators the
procedure thereafter more or less follows similar lines to that as used
for Pheasants.

QUAIL

The North American Quails are the only species propagated in any
numbers, and even then not all species are propagated and then not
very extensively. Since they are Monogamous, pens or wire coops are
used to house breeding pairs from which the eggs are transferred to
incubators, and because of the very small size of the resulting chicks
the resulting accommodation and procedures are very much minia-
turised versions of those for Pheasants and Partridges.

GROUSE, TURKEY AND SNOWCOCKS

At different times attempts have been made, with varying degrees
of success, to restock or acclimatise certain species of these birds
in various countries, Capercaillie in Scotland successfully and North
America unsuccessfully; in France and Germany it is early days yet,
as with Italy.

Figure 15.   **Laying Pen for Grouse**

Figure A

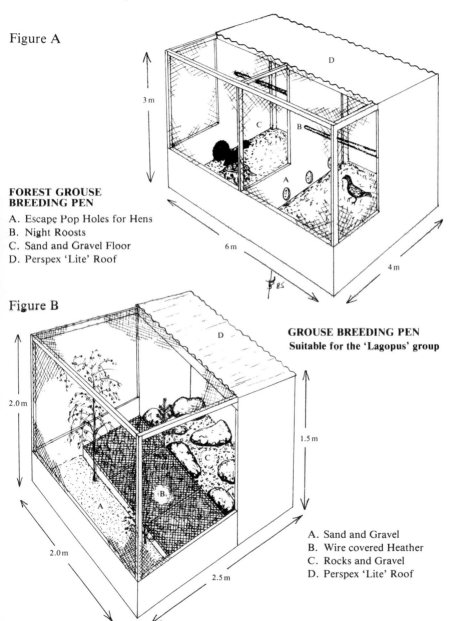

**FOREST GROUSE
BREEDING PEN**

A. Escape Pop Holes for Hens
B. Night Roosts
C. Sand and Gravel Floor
D. Perspex 'Lite' Roof

Figure B

**GROUSE BREEDING PEN
Suitable for the 'Lagopus' group**

A. Sand and Gravel
B. Wire covered Heather
C. Rocks and Gravel
D. Perspex 'Lite' Roof

Turkeys have been tried in Scotland and eventually failed; in Germany efforts come and go but will hopefully end in failure too. Snowcocks have been tried in the USA, fortunately with the same lack of success as with Capercaillie. It may be fairly gathered that I do not approve of establishing alien species outside their natural distribution and would suggest that energies of this type would be better directed at improving numbers of the native species, as has been done very successfully with the Greater Pinnated Grouse in some parts of the northern United States.

A great deal of research and effort has been devoted to the husbandry of the Scottish Red Grouse and it does seem unlikely that either this species or any other Ptarmigan can be reared in numbers for hunting using birds bred and reared in captivity.

In Scandinavia and Germany considerable efforts are being devoted to researching the possibilities for propagating numbers of Black Grouse and Capercaillie, but it does seem unlikely to get beyond the stage of the re-stocking of empty areas in either species' distribution which in itself is a highly useful and worthwhile objective.

Figure 16. **Laying Pen for Pheasant**

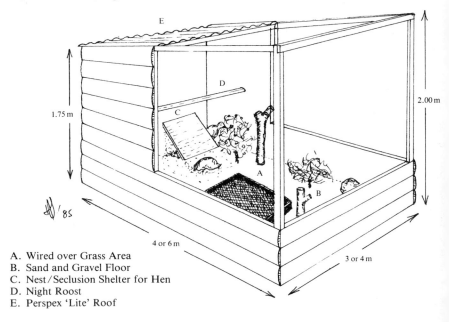

A. Wired over Grass Area
B. Sand and Gravel Floor
C. Nest/Seclusion Shelter for Hen
D. Night Roost
E. Perspex 'Lite' Roof

Chapter 4.6
Hygiene & Veterinary Care in Captivity

The purpose of this section of the book is to outline the general principles concerning the health of birds in captivity, particularly those in Aviculture. It is not the intention to provide advice on Veterinary care but only to outline general sound practice for Aviculturalists where this may involve management of captive birds.

There is a very comprehensive list of reference papers listed in Appendix I and I would recommend consultation of the Appendix for more in-depth information on many aspects of Veterinary care.

While it will be obvious that a great deal of study has already been undertaken in respect to Gallinaceous birds and their health, there is clearly a lot more work to be done and a fuller understanding needed of the implications for both captive and wild populations. In this chapter I propose to confine myself to a basic outline insofar as Aviculture is concerned and deal with the general aspects.

When deciding on one's approach to captive husbandry at the planning stage there are a number of variables which ought to be considered. To this end I will presume to make an assumption which, put simply, is that of specialisation in a certain group or groups of birds. Holding to the basic view that while the other approach to Aviculture might look beautiful in the short-term, it will, in the long-term, be found to be ill-conceived. Sooner or later we all arrive at the same conclusion by one route or another, usually hastened by the urge for professional care of the birds for whose welfare we are responsible.

Some points I would offer as being very important when drawing up your basics before moving forward include the following:–

1. Soil depth.
2. Drainage.
3. Composition and acidity.
4. Rainfall.
5. Wind direction, frequency and velocity.
6. Proneness to certain ailments based on other peoples' experience under similar climactic conditions.
7. Exposure or proximity to species likely to carry infections while not being themselves similarly affected to any great extent.
8. Temperature and humidity ranges.

At this juncture it would be well worth listing some of the more frequently encountered ailments, obvious symptoms and suggested means to avoid occurrence. There is a well known axiom – prevention is better than cure. Its repetition here in no way detracts from the wisdom of the saying, as I can personally testify. On more than one occasion I have either said, "It won't happen to me", or, "I must remember to do that, next week definitely". Somehow it does happen to me and somehow I never do remember – with the result of extra work at best, or disaster in the form of deaths at worst.

To lose any birds through avoidable deaths is bad enough, but the sheer frustration of losing, for example, a cock bird only to have the hen start laying three weeks later, as has happened to me, leads to much wailing and gnashing of teeth, especially when it was avoidable and your own fault.

Fowl Pest, also known as *Newcastle Disease*, is possibly the best to begin with due to it being perhaps the worst possible disease found amongst the Gallinaceous birds. This viral disease best illustrates "prevention is better than cure" as it is possible to vaccinate against infection. However, once your birds contract the disease they have no hope of recovery. If they get it, they have had it! Innoculation with either live or dead vaccine can be made into either the leg or breast muscles. Alternatives include an eyedrop live vaccine for day old chicks, or also it is possible to administer a live vaccine in drinking water. Living as I do in Scotland this is one of the few diseases no likely to prove a problem, but in England and elsewhere, periodic dosing of adult birds is recommended – ideally in February and August.

In the United Kingdom, Fowl Pest is a notifiable disease, subject to rigorous controls and a slaughter policy. It is for this reason that because Scotland is disease free all birds imported even from England are subject to full quarantine control.

Coccidiosis is especially likely to manifest itself under intensive rearing conditions, causing considerable disruption especially at the poult stage. Where soil conditions are frequently damp, either through high rainfall and/or poor drainage, Coccidiosis is more likely to occur.

This disease is a particularly virulent form of enteritis which if untreated will result in extensive losses. The birds' droppings, frequent and whitish, often even showing traces of blood, are the clearest indication of infection. At the same time the birds move about slowly with slack feathers, wings drooping and head either hunched or carried low and forward.

In rearing young birds feed can be purchased incorporating a controlling drug; however, when treatment of infected birds is necessary either a sulpha drug or a broad spectrum antibiotic can be used.

Blackhead is commonly associated with the Turkey but is equally disastrous to Grouse and Pheasants, also most probably Quail. This disease is transmitted by the caecal worm *Heterakis gallinae* as a carrier of the *Histomonas meleagridis* protozoa and can be treated either as a premix in the feed or water. As a precaution it is prudent to dose all incoming birds before allowing them near your collection.

Symptoms of this disease are quickly obvious with yellow or green loose droppings and the overall dejected appearance of birds similar to that seen in birds suffering from Coccidiosis. The important difference to be stressed is that shown by the colour of the birds' droppings.

Sinusitis is a nasal infection more often found in poults and identfiable by wet discharges from the nostrils and bubbly foam at the corner of the eyes. Treatment is by a water-soluble drug.

Gapeworm or *Syngamu trachea* is a nematode worm known as 'Gapes' from the birds' repeated gaping and head shaking in an effort to dislodge the parasitic worms from its trachea.

The life cycle commences with male and female worms mated together in a distinctive Y shape visible to the naked eye. These worms attach themselves by the mouth parts through which nourishment is absorbed from the host. Fertilised eggs eventually passed out of the vent in the birds' droppings develop into a larvae after 3−4 days when they are potentially able to actively reinfect a new host or the original one. If they are not picked up at this stage the worms hatch at nine days and are self-supporting, being capable of infection of alternative hosts such as earthworms or other invertibrates, some of which are in turn eaten by birds, so that the cycle resumes with the worm returning from the gut to lodge in the trachea, thereby increasing the burden for the bird and resuming the reproductive cycle in around two weeks'.

Gapeworm infestation, and Coccidiosis are the two likeliest forms of illness to be encountered, and both can be pre-empted with good hygiene procedures. In the event of an outbreak of either it is suggested that after dealing with the problem and its effects it would be prudent to review all aspects of your management as objectively as possible. To moan about your losses using phrases like "I can't imagine how", or, "why me" is to invite a repeat performance. These infections do not arrive or move in mysterious ways. They do not happen accidentally; they happen through at best simple ignorance, error or just downright incompetence. I must also admit to it happening to me − more than once as well!

There are a number of veterinary products made by various companies using their own brand names. These change with improvement and perhaps to list a few might not be very helpful. Perhaps as a matter of policy one should have a 'quick action' pack on hand as advised by your own Vet who could undertake visits, say half yearly or quarterly, make observations, review the position and run tests on faecal samples perhaps.

For reference purposes there is an Appendix of papers on veterinary aspects which may be useful for anyone needing to follow a line of enquiry at any time.

ARTIFICIAL INSEMINATION
OF GAMEBIRDS

Formerly a subject surrounded by somewhat intimidatory terminology and only practised by the very few; nowadays, however, A.I. (as it is known for short) is much more widely practised throughout the world, by professionals and amateurs alike. Put simply, A.I. is a technique resorted to in order to take semen from a male of a species and transfer it to the female in an effort to fertilise the female inducing, as a result, a successful breeding.

There are several reasons why it may be necessary for such a procedure to be adopted and these are listed below.

1. **Injury.** Where the Cock bird is temporarily or permanently disabled; perhaps a wing or leg injury which either completely prevents the bird from mating or which is likely to lead to a doubtful coupling and fertilisation.

2. **Imprinted.** Where the Cock bird is imprinted in some way, either to a human or another animate object not its proper mate, semen can be extracted very easily, the bird often being more than willing to oblige.

3. **Geographical.** Where birds of low numbers and high inbreeding are found in like groups across National or extreme Continental distances involving perhaps unwillingness to part with valuable specimens, difficulties of movement, licences or quarantine restrictions.

4. **Physcological.** Especially where birds are repeatedly inbred over numerous generations Cocks have a declining libido which ultimately proves to be totally lacking. The birds are not in fact infertile in any way; they just are not interested in reproductive energies or behaviour and cannot even be bothered to display to their Hens, who are just ignored.

5. **Numerical.** Where the birds involved are, for example, Monogamous but there happens to be perhaps a single Cock and five Hens, clearly only one pair are likely to be bred from which would leave four Hens as unproductive — when the relatively short repro-

ductive lifetime of most birds is taken into account there are obvious risks in this. As a management tool, however, the single Cock bird is used for A.I. therefore also fertilising each of the other Hens and even if used only once per Hen, most, if not all, the clutch should prove fertile.

If the results shoud prove to be worth the effort there is no reason why two clutches might not be obtained. This is neither greedy nor unwarranted, for where Aviculturists are in possession of birds limited in numbers they have an absolute obligation to maximise production from those few that they do have in order to better secure those in captivity.

Artificial Insemination as a procedure is basically very simple and really only requires patience and slow, delicate but firm and deliberate actions. It would be true to say that while women are usually better not only at sexing chicks but at A.I. too, due apparently to their generally smaller hands and more gentle approach, regardless of who undertakes A.I. anyone of a nervous or excitable nature is really not the ideal sort of person.

The procedure has been used for quite some time with the heavier strains of Domestic Turkeys which are unable to mount their Hens, or when they do the Hen's back is often damaged under the Cock's weight and spurs. A very useful procedure is for intending practitioners to develop the simple but valuable skill through working with Domestic Poultry, Cockerels and Hens.

It is extremely difficult to operate by oneself, and very much easier with two, but ideally three people make the best and most effective team. Without rushing at it, a reasonable rate of progress is important and this can be greatly assisted by adequate preparation. This preparation covers most importantly hygiene, proper implements and secure accommodation.

It is highly unnecessary to charge around after the birds, catching them up, hanging onto them and probably getting covered in muck at the same time. If possible an overnighting by all birds involved in a small but adequate coop, one per bird to avoid confusion if more than one Hen is involved, is particularly useful. It can only be advantageous to reduce the amount of stress to the absolute minimum.

If there is a team of three, one of these will be responsible for holding the Cock bird. The second person will be involved in manipulating the Cock bird while the third person collects the semen on a glass pipette. The first person holding the Cock bird can either be seated with the bird laid out on his or her lap, feet towards the knees and head up towards the waist, or alternatively the bird may be laid on a pad placed on a small table or bench; in either case the bird is lying on its back, with its head lightly covered to eliminate sight temporarily, wings firmly held close to the body and legs parallel, but slightly apart at more or less the natural spacing.

The Hen is similarly held with the vent presented forward; if possible the head too should be lightly covered. With both birds the head can be put into the darkness at the side of a jacket if one is worn, or under a woollen jersey, for example.

Obviously while the first person is holding the Cock bird the person elected to hold the Hen bird is involved in fact in manipulating the Cock bird. This is done by applying a light pressure with the flat of one hand against the abdomen while gently stroking the bird's feathers from between the hips towards the vent. Providing the bird is in reproductive condition this procedure should result in the production of semen. It is well worth bearing in mind that like all other creatures each bird will have its own personality and be less or more inclined to co-operate than others might be. To quote two extremes, I once had a male European Crane which would not only rush to jump on to my lap but would defend me against other humans, all of whom were female, which could be a bit cramping. The other was an ordinary Rhode Island Red Cockerel who on reflection was perhaps not quite so ordinary. He could not stand being touched by anybody or anything unless he wanted to initiate the contact, which invariably was unpleasant, especially if you were a Duck or a Drake peacefully lying sleeping, only to wake up abruptly to find a perverted red feather-duster sitting on top of you. Known as 'Little Duncan', that was one bird which I rather enjoyed 'freezer training'.

On producing the semen, it is collected by the second person using a glass pipette which is a small hollow glass tube roughly 60–80cm long with a tapered point, having at the opposite end a small rubber diaphragm. When collecting the semen the diaphragm is depressed, the tip is placed against the semen and the diaphragm is released, resulting in the fluid being sucked into the glass pipette.

When the transfer has been achieved the first person who has been holding the Cock bird can then gently return that bird to its temporary coop, where if he stands and ruffles his feathers and preens it means he is well pleased with himself. Having put back the Cock the operator then picks up the Hen bird and gently places it in position, making sure the bird's wings are firmly held in place; it is essential to avoid struggling and the associated stress which goes with that. Using the fingers of the free hand, the 'Gloaca' is inverted gently, at which point the pipette is presented with the tip being carefully inserted and the diaphragm depressed again which should result in the semen being injected into place. When the semen is in place the Gloaca is gently allowed to revert to the natural position and it can then be very lightly and gently massaged.

With reasonable good fortune the resulting eggs should in fact prove fertile but the procedure can be repeated two or three times every three days or so. It should be remembered that if the Hen is already in lay, which is the best time for Gamebirds (that is, as soon as the first egg appears) the resulting first or second eggs are unlikely to be fertile as they will already have commenced development in the bird's reproductive system.

Where semen is being collected for storage, and/or storage and despatch, the manipulation of the Hen is obviously not considered but a new procedure is implemented involving depositing the semen in sterile 'straws' which are then frozen, maintained and transported in this way until used. For those wanting to use this system it is best to refer you to either the local Veterinary College, Department of Agriculture or Universities' Natural Sciences Departments where expert advice and assistance can be enlisted.

In conclusion, if ever hygiene was vital and fundamental then it is for A.I. procedures, but having said that there is no reason to be intimidated – a good dose of common sense goes a long way and there is no reason why anyone who needs to use this valuable aid to Aviculture and Conservation should not do so.

Appendix I

**ROYAL COLLEGE OF VETERINARY
SURGEONS' WELLCOME LIBRARY**

SE 3/249A

**Gamebirds:
Management & Diseases**

Revised:
December 1978

1. ABBOTT, U. K. and CHRISTENSEN, G. C. (1971). *Hatching and rearing the Himalayan Snow Partridge in captivity.* J. Wildl. Mgmt. *35:* 301–306.

2. AIGNER, R. (1977). *Chromium, Cobalt and Nickel Contents in the Tissues of Field Hares, Pheasants and Partridges.* Wien tierärztl. Mschr. *64* (11): 333. German.

3. ANDERSON, W. C. (1969). *Condition Parameters and Organ Measurements of Pheasants from Good, Fair and Poor Range in Illinois.* J. Wildl. Mgmt. *33:* 979–987.

4. ANGOT, André (1973). *Animaux Nuisibles et Gibier dans le Département de la Manche.* Alfort, Thesis.

5. AVERBECK, Anton (1971). *Beitrag zur Prage der Ernährung des Rebhuhns (Perdix Perdix L.) in der Kulturlandschaft.* Hannover, Inaug.-Diss., 83 pp.

6. BAKER, K. B. and WESTWOOD, A. (1971). *Erysipelas in the Guinea-Fowl.* Vet. Rec. *88:* 108–109.

7. BEJSOVEC, J. (1978). *Ecological Influences on the Dynamics of Distribution of the Coccidia Eimeria Phasiani and Eimeria Colchici.* Angewandt. Parasitol. *19* (2): 76–85. German, English summ.

8. BEJSOVEC, J. (1974). *I. Specificity of Coccidians of Wild Galliform Birds under Conditions of Prolonged Contact among various host species. II. The incidence of Eimeria Colchici Norton, 1967 and Eimeria Phasiani Tyzzer, 1929 in various Biotypes of an Agricultural Landscape.* J. Protozool. *21* (3): 454.

9. BERKHOFF, G. A. (1974). *Etiology of Ulcerative Enteritis (quail disease)*. J. Am. vet. med. Ass. *165* (8): 744.

10. BINDER, François (1971). *Organisation, Production et Controle de l'élévage du Gibier en France*. Alfort, thesis.

11. BLANK, T. H. (1972). *The Preservation of Wild Animals in Sport*. Br. vet. J. *128* (8): 381–85.

12. BONNEAU, N. H. and FILIAN, R. (1973). *Réparation d'une Fracture Fémorale et Extraction de Corps Etrangers dans le Gésier Chez un Faisan*. Cas clinique. Can. vet. J. *14* (5): 119–121.

13. BORG, Karl (1953). *On Leucocytozoon in Swedish Capercaillie Black Grouse and Hazel Grouse*. Lund, Berlingska Boktryockeriet, 109pp.

14. BORLAND, E. D. (1977). *A Field Study of Mortality in Pheasant Chicks*. Vet. Rec. *100* (9): 175–176.

15. BORLAND, E. D. (1976). *Outbreak of Botulism in Reared East Anglian Pheasants (corresp.)*. Vet. Rec. *99* (11): 220–221.

16. BORLAND, E. D. (1972). *Newcastle Disease in Pheasants, Partridges and Wild Birds in East Anglia 1970–1971*. Vet. Rec. *90* (17): 481–482.

17. BOUGEROL, Christian (1968). *Essai sur la Pathologie des Oiseaux de Chasse au Vol*. Alfort, Thesis, 60pp.

18. BUNYAN, P. J. and JENNINGS, D. M. (1976). *Carbamate Poisoning. Effect of Certain Carbamate Pesticides on Esterase Levels in the Pheasant (Phasianius Colchicus) and Pigeon (Columba Livia)*. J. Agr. Food. Chem. *24* (1): 136–143.

19. BUXTON, D. and REID, H. W. (1975). *Experimental Infection of Red Grouse with Loupingill Virus (Flavivirus Group) II. Neuropathology*. J. comp. Path. *85* (2): 231–235.

20. BYGRAVE, A. C. (1971). *An Outbreak of Erysipelas in Pheasant Poults (Phasianus Colchicus)*. Vet. Rec. *89* (10): 279. Scientific correspondence.

21. BYGRAVE, A. C. and PATTISON, M. (1973). *Marble Spleen Disease in Pheasants (Phasianus Colchicus)*. Scientific correspondence. Vet. Rec. *92* (20): 534–535.

22. CAIN, J. R. *et al* (1976). *Dietary Influence on Growth and Cannibalism in Pheasants*. Poultry Sci. *55* (5): 2014.

23. CARLSON, H. C. *et al* (1973). *Marble Spleen Disease Pheasants in Ontario*. Can. J. comp. Med. *37* (3): 281–286.

24. CHEN, Y. C. and VOGT, P. K. (1977). *Endogenous Leukosis Viruses in the Avian Family Phasianidae*. Virology *76* (2): 740–750.

25. CHEVALIER, Francis (1968). *La Caille Domestique*. Alfort, thesis., 62pp.

26. COLES, C. L. (1974). *Game as a Farm Crop.* J. Roy. Agr. Soc. England *135:* 55–60.

27. CONNAN, R. M. and WISE, D. R. (1977). *Efficacy of Tetramisole and Dichloroxylenol against Syngamus Trachea in Pheasants and Turkeys.* Vet. Rec. *101* (2): 34–35.

28. DELANE, T. M. and HAYWARD, J. S. (1975). *Acclimatisation to Temperature in Pheasants (Phasianus Colchicus) and Partridge (Perdix Perdix).* Comp. Biochem. Physiol. *51A* (3): 531–536.

29. DEVOS, A. *et al* (1975). *Tuberculosis in Game Pheasants.* Vlaams Diergeneesk. Tijdschr. *44* (1): 19–24. Dutch, English summ.

30. DEVOS, A. H. and VIAENE, J. (1975). *Tuberculosis in Game Pheasants and Public Health. IN* 20th World Vet. Congr., Thessaloniki Summaries *2:* 1083–1084.

31. DOMERMUTH, C. H. *et al* (1977). *Serologic Examination of Wild Birds for Hemorrhagic Enteritis of Turkey and Marble Spleen Disease of Pheasants.* J. Wildl. Dis. *13* (4): 405–8.

32. DZHAMGYRCHIEVA, T. D. *et al* (1975). *Wild Birds as Carriers of Pathogenic Micro-organisms. IN Infektsionnye Bolezni Zhivotnykh i Voprosy Prirodnoi Ochagivost (Infectious Diseases of Animals and Problems of Natural Nidality)* ed. by A. A. Volkova, Frunze, Kirgizskaya SSR, Izdatel'stvo"Ilim": 88–93; 127. Russian.

33. FALK, Josefine Wilhelmine (1973). *Ein Beitrag zur Frage der Haltungsmöglichkeiten des Rothuhnes (alectoris rufa) in Norddeutschland.* Hannover, Inaug.-Diss., 97pp.

34. FARUGA, A. and PUCHAJDA, H. (1976). *Effect of some Husbandry Methods on the Results of Fattening Young Guinea Fowl.* Medycyna Wet. *32* (7): 426–428. Polish, English summ.

35. FEDORENKO, I. O. (1973). *Phthiraptera of Game Birds in the Ukraine. Paraziti, Parazitozi ta Shlyakhi ikh Likvidatsii* (2): 92–95. Ukrainian, English summ.

36. FEVERL, M. (1975). *Capercaillie and Black Grouse: their Natural Habitat and Maintenance in Captivity with reference to the Possibility of their reintroduction into the Wild. A Report on the Preservation and Husbandry of these Grouse.* Hannover, Inaug.-Diss., 130pp. German.

37. FISHER, J. W. and WACHA, R. S. (1976). *Coccidian Parasites from Game-Farm Reared Pheasants, Phasianus Colchicus, in Iowa.* Procs. Helminth. Soc. Washington *43* (2): 226–27.

38. FUJITA, D. J. *et al* (1974). *Endogenous Leukosis Viruses of Pheasants. IN Viral Transformation and Endogenous Viruses.* Procs. 1974 Abraham Flexner Symp. Vanderbilt Univ., Tennessee, USA., April 1-2, 1974. New York, Academic Press: 159–171.

39. GAME ADVISORY STATION (197-?). *Pheasant Rearing.* Fordingbridge, Hants. G.A.S.

40. GAME CONSERVATION (1976). *Some Diesease of Game Birds and Wildlife.* Fordingbridge, Hants. Game Conservancy booklet 6, 58pp.

41. GÉRAL, M. F. *et al* (1976). *Experimental Infection of Game Birds (Pheasant, Red-Legged Partridge and Grey Partridge) with Newcastle Disease Virus.* Rév. Méd. vét. *127* (11): 1537−1574. French, English summ.

42. GERRITS, H. A. (1961). *Pheasants, including Their Care in the Aviary;* illustrations by H. J. Slijper. London, Blandford Press, 144pp.

43. GORDON, R. F. *Ed.* (1977). *Poultry Diseases.* London. Baillière Tindall, 352pp.

44. GROLLEAU, G. and PARIS, G. (1973). *Toxicity of 2-Chloro-4-Toluidine to the Partridge (Perdix Perdix) and the Red-Legged Partridge (Alectoris Rufa).* Ann. Zool. Ecol. Anim. *5* (1): 139−141. French.

45. HANSSEN, I. (1975). *Listeriosis among Willow Grouse (Lagopus Lagopus) in Captivity.* Nord. Vet. Med. *27* (1): 37−41.

46. HANSSEN, I. (1975). *Pulmonary Phycomycosis in Captive Rock Ptarmigan (Lagopus Mutus) and Willow Ptarmigan (Lagopus Lagopus) Chicks.* Acta vet. scand. *16* (1): 134−136.

47. HARRISON, G. (1974). *Clostridium Botulinum Type C Infection on a Game Fowl Farm.* IN Am. Ass. Zoo Vet. Ann. Procs., 1974. Atlanta, Georgia: 221−224.

48. ILTIS, J. P. and DANIELS, S. B. (1977). *Adenovirus of Ring-Necked Pheasants: Purification and Partial Characterisation of Marble Spleen Disease Virus.* Infect. and Immun. *16* (2): 701−705.

49. ILTIS, J. P. and WYAWD, D. S. (1974). *Indications of Viral Etiology for Marble Spleen Disease in Pheasants.* J. Wildl. Dis. *10* (3): 272−278.

50. HOFSTAD, M. S. *et al, eds.* (1972). *Diseases of Poultry, Ames (Iowa),* The Iowa State Univ. Press, 1176pp.

51. JACOBSEN, G. S. *et al* (1976). *An Epornitic of Duck Plague on a Wisconsin Game Farm.* J. Wildl. Dis. *12* (1): 20−26.

52. KASZUBKIEWICZ, C. and SOLTYSIAK, Z. (1976). *Tuberculosis in Game Pheasants.* Medycyna Wet. *32* (9): 530−532. Polish, English summ.

53. KOJNOK, J. *et al* (1976). *Attempts for Immunisation of Partridges (Perdix Perdix) against Newcastle Disease.* Acta vet. Acad. Sci. Hung. *26* (2): 209−213.

54. KRAFT, E. (1972). *Comparative Morphological Studies on the Individual Bones of the Smaller Gallinaceous Birds of Northern and Central Europe.* München, Inaug.-Diss., 195pp. German, English summ.

55. KULCZYCKI, A. (1975). *The Effect of the Organophosphate Insecticides Nogos (Dichlorvos) and Ouradofos (Fenitrothion) on Survival Rate and Reproduction in Pheasants (Phasianus colchicus)*. Acta Agraria et Silvestria, Ser. Zootech. *15* (2): 63–72. Polish, English summ.

56. LAGE, M. *et al* (1974). *Comparison of the Pathogenicity of a Velogenic Strain of Newcastle Disease Virus for Various Species of Galliformes (Pheasant, Fowl, Guinea-Fowl, Turkey, Quail)*. Atti Soc. ital. Sci. vet. *28:* 746–750. Italian, English summ.

57. LALLEMANT, G. (1975). *Hunting and Farming. A Study on the Decline in Game, Proposals for Improvement*. Alfort, thesis, 58 pp. French.

58. LESLIE, A. S. *ed.* assisted by SHIPLEY, A. E. (1912). *The Grouse in Health and Disease: Being the Popular Edition of the Report of the Committee of Inquiry on Grouse Disease*. London, Smith, Edler & Co., 472 pp.

59. LORGUE, G. and SOYEZ, D. (1976). *Study of the Toxic Effects of the Dithiocarbamate Fungicide, Thiram, in Partridges*. II. Bull. Soc. Sci. vét. Méd. comp. Lyon *78* (5): 279–288. French.

60. LOUZIS, C. (1976). *Isolation of Chlamydia Psittaci from Artificially Reared Grey Partridge*. Bull. Acad. vét. France *49* (2): 201–204. French.

61. LOUZIS, C. *et al* (1978). *Use of Immunoelectrophoresis to Diagnose Marble Spleen Disease of Pheasants Reared in Captivity*. Rév. Méd. vét. *129* (5): 761–762; 765–771. French, English summ.

62. MADSEN, H. (1966). *On Feather Picking and Cannibalism in Pheasant and Partridge Chicks, particularly in relation to the Amino Acid Arginine*. Acta vet. scand. *7:* 272–287.

63. MADSEN, H. (1969). *Sexing Day-Old Game Pheasant Chicks*. Dan. Rev. Game Biol. *5* (7): 8.

64. MEIGNIER, B. *et al* (1977). *Experimental Infection of Game Birds (Pheasant, Red and Grey Partridge) with Fowl Pox Virus*. Rév. méd. vét. *128* (1): 83–86; 89–94. French, English summ.

65. MENCHACA, E. S. *et al* (1977). *Newcastle Disease in Pheasants*. Revta Med. vet., Argentina *58* (4): 367–368. Spanish.

66. MERENYI, L. *et al* (1978). *Perforation of the Gizzard in a Guinea-Fowl caused by a Foreign Body*. Magyar Allatorv. Lap. *33* (4): 280–281. Hungarian.

67. MESSICK, J. P. *et al* (1974). *Aerial Pesticide Applications and Ring-Necked Pheasants*. J. Wildl. Mgmt. *38* (4): 679–685.

68. MICHAUT, Lucien (1962). *Conditions du Bon Repeuplement d'une Chasse en Faisans*. Paris, Thesis.

69. MORROW, J. L. and TAYLOR, D. H. (1976). *A Telemetry System for Recording Heart Rates of Unrestrained Game Birds*. J. Wildl. Mgmt. *40* (2): 359–360.

70. MULLER, H. (1978). *Erysipelas in Phesants*. Mh. Vet. Med. *33* (5): 173–175.
     German, English summ.

71. MULLINS, W. H. *et al* (1977). *Effects of Phenyl Mercury on Captive Game
     Farm Pheasants*. J. Wildl. Mgmt. *41* (2): 302–308.

72. NATH, Dharmendra (1973). *Experimental Development of Prosthogonimus
     ovatus* (Rud. 1803) LUHE, 1899 *in Common Quails, Grey Partridges and
     Guinea Fowls*. Indian vet. J. *50* (5): 465–473.

73. NEVEUX, André (1951). *Contribution à l'Étude de la Diminution de la Perdix
     en France. Sea Causes, Moyens d'y Remédier*. Paris, Thesis.

74. OUDAR, J. *et al* (1975). *Bacteriological Study of 148 Strains of Escherichia
     coli Isolated from Partridges*. Rév. méd. vét. *126* (12): 1693–1710; 1713–1718.
     French, English summ.

75. OUDAR, J. *et al* (1974). *Three Serious Outbreaks of Erysipelothrix insidiosa
     Infections in Red-Legged Partridges bred in Captivity*. Bull. Soc. Sci. vét.
     Méd. Lyon *76* (2): 105–110. French.

76. PASCUCCI, S. *et al* (1976). *Mycoplasma Synoviae in the Guinea-Fowl*. Avian
     Path. *5* (4): 291–297.

77. PAV, J. and ZAJICEK, D. (1974). *Parasites of Grouse and Capercaillie in
     Czechoslovakia. Preserves in the Hunting Season*. Veterinarstvi *24* (11):
     517–520. Czech.

78. PETTIT, J. R. *et al* (1976). *Microscopic Lesions suggestive of Marek's Disease
     in a Black Francolin (Francolinus f. francolinus)*. Avian Dis. *20* (2): 410–415.

79. PIEDVACITE, Y. H. F. (1973). *Study of the Biology and Breeding of the
     Common and Red-Legged Partridges*. Alfort, thesis.

80. POTTS, G. R. (1974). *Partridges: Survival and Disease*. Vet. Rec. *95* (6): 129.

81. PULLAINEN, E. (1965). *Cannibalism in the Pheasant (Phasainus colchicus)
     the Egg-Laying Period*. Annals. zo.

82. PUROHIT, V. D. *et al* (1977). *Persistent Right Oviduct in Ring-Necked
     Pheasant*. Br. Poultry Sci. *18* (2): 177–178.

83. PURSGLOVE, S. R. (1974). *Some Parasites and Diseases of the American
     Woodcock, Philohela minor (Gmelin)*. Diss. Abstr. Int. *34B* (9): 4746–4747.

84. RATH, H. (1977). *Determination of Lead, Cadmium and Zinc in Tissues of
     Field Hares, Partridges and Pheasants*. Wien. tierärztl. Mschr. *64* (5): 168–
     169. German.

85. REDON, P. and TOURNUT, J. (1973). *Transmissible Enteritis of Young
     Partridges*. Révue Méd. vét. *124* (6): 743–756.

86. REID, H. W. (1975). *Experimental Infection of Red Grouse with Louping-Ill
     Virus (Flavivirus Group). I. The Viraemia and Antibody Response*. J. comp.
     Path. *85* (2): 223–229.

87. REID, H. W. and BOYCE, J. B. (1974). *Louping-Ill Virus in Red Grouse in Scotland*. Vet. Rec. *95* (7): 150.

88. REVILLA, P. S. (1974). *Current Knowledge of the Infections and Parasitic Diseases of Quail. I. Bacterial and Mycotic Infections. II. Viral Infections. III. Parasitic Infections*. Veterinaria, Spain *39* (2, 3/4, 5/6): 69–78, 119–128, 191–199. Spanish.

89. RICO, A. G. *et al* (1976). *Biometry, Haematology, Blood and Tissue Enzymatology in the Grey Partridge*. Ann. Rech. Vét. *7* (4): 315–328. French, English summ.

90. RICO, A. G. *et al* (1977). *Biometry, Haematology, Plasma Biochemistry and Plasma and Tissue Enzymology of the Red Partridge (Alectoris rufa)*. Ann. Rech. Vét. *8* (3): 251–256. French, English summ.

91. RODRIGUEZ, J. R. and HERRERA, J. L. (1974). *Eimeria Padulensis n.sp. from Alectoris rufa (Red-Legged Partridge): a Description of the Parasite Morphology*. Revta Iber. Parasitol *34* (1/2): 29–31. Spanish, English summ.

92. ROMIC, S. (1975). *Fertility of the Partridge (Perdix perdix) between 1933 and 1966*. Poljop. Znanst. Smotra *35:* 167–184. Serbo-croat. English summ.

93. SCHULTE, T. and PORTER, W. P. (1974). *Environmental Limitations of Pheasant Egg Hatching Success*. Auk *91* (3): 522–531.

94. SMETANA, P. (1971). *Pheasant Raising*. J. Agric. West Aust. 4th Ser. *12:* 280–281.

95. SOUCHELEAU, Gerard (1961). *Contribution a l'Étude de l'Elevage du Faisan de Chasse*. Alfort, Thesis, 48 pp.

96. STREIB, A. *et al* (1973). *Pheasants*. Ottawa, Canada Dept. Agric.

97. STROMBORG, K. L. (1977). *Seed Treatment Pesticide Effects on Pheasant Reproduction at Sublethal Doses*. J. Wildl. Mgmt. *41* (4): 632–642.

98. STROMBORG, K. L. (1975). *Sub-lethal Effects of Seed Treatment Pesticides on Breeding Hen Pheasants*. Diss. Abstr. Int. *36B* (6): 2547–2548.

99. SWARBRICK, Olaf (1973). *Inclusion Body Hepatitis in Pheasants (corresp.)*. Vet. Rec. *93* (7): 209.

100. SWARUP, M. and CHAUHAN, M. P. S. (1976). *Eimeria Francolin n.sp. (Protozoa: Eimeridae) from a Black Partridge, Francolinus francolinus*. Science & Culture *42* (3): 166–167.

101. *Symposium on the Nutrition of New Farm Animals,* 8th November 1974, Glasgow. Procs. Nutr. Soc. *34* (1): 51–100.

102. SZTOTKOV. V. *et al* (1978). *"Marble Spleen Disease" of Pheasants in Hungary*. Magyar allatorv. Lap. *33* (4): 223–226. Hungarian, English summ.

103. TAYLOR, E. L. G. (1976). *Avian Tuberculosis. An Experimental Attempt at Control in a Breeding Flock or Ornamental Pheasants. IN World Pheasant Ass. J. 1975–1976:* 59–61.

104. TRION, Francis (1971). *Le Cannibalism Chex le Faisan.* Alfort, Thesis.

105. THOMAS, V. G. and BAILEY, E. D. (1973). *Influence of Date of Egg-Production and Diet in Pheasant Chick Development.* Can. J. Zool. *51* (11): 1149–1154.

106. TIMONEY, P. J. (1972). *Recovery of Louping-Ill Virus from the Red Grouse in Ireland.* Br. vet. J. *128* (1): 19–23.

107. TIONG, S. K. (1978). *Isolation of Mycoplasma gallisepticum from Sinuses of Three Quails (Coturnix coturnix) japonica).* Vet. Rec. *103* (24): 539.

108. VLADIK, P. *et al* (1975). *Listeriosis and Aspergillosis in the Pheasant (Phasianus colchicus).* Veterinarstvi 25 (12): 566–567. Czech.

109. WERNER, U. (1975). *Comparison of the Brain and Body Weights of Pheasants Reared in Captivity and Wild Pheasants.* Hannover, Inaug.-Diss., 68 pp. German, English summ.

110. WETZEL, R. and RIECK, W. (1973). *Diseases of Game Animals.* Hamburg, Paul Parey. (In German).

111. WISE, D. R. (1974). *Pheasants: Husbandry and Diseases.* Vet. Rec. *95* (6): 129.

112. WISSLER, K. and HALVORSEN, O. (1975). *The Occurrence of Gapeworm (Syngamus trachea) in Willow Grouse.* J. Wildl. Dis. *11* (2): 245–247.

113. WOEHLER, E. E. and GATES, J. M. (1970). *An Improved Method of Sexing Ring Necked Pheasant Chicks.* J. Wildl. Mgmt. *34:* 228–231.

114. WOOD, N. A. (1969). *Formic Acid as a Prophylactic for Candidiasis in Partridges.* Vet. Rec. *85:* 78–81.

115. WOOD, N. A. (1970). *Treatment of Established Infections of Candidiasis in Partridges with Formic Acid.* Vet. Rec. *87:* 656–658.

I would like to acknowledge the assistance of my brother Douglas Brodie, BVMS, MRCVS, who was kind enough to obtain works of reference with the invaluable co-operation of the Wellcome Library, Royal College of Veterinary Science.

Appendix II

LIST OF SUPPLIERS & MANUFACTURERS

Louis E. Page Inc., P.O. Box 405, Littleton, Mass. 01460.
Welded Wire Fabric, Hardware Cloth, etc.

Safeguard Products Inc., 114-116 Earland Drive, New Holland, PA, 17557.
Incubators, Hatchers, Breeding & Growing Pens/Cages

Iain Brodie, Cuilalun, Kinchurdy Road, Boat of Garten, Inverness-shire.
Distributors for Safeguard

National Band and Tag Co., Dept. 4-430, Newport, KY 41072.
Leg Bands & Wing Tags

Reliable Thermostat Co. Ltd., Main Street, Bramley, Yorks. S66 0SD.
Incubators, Thermostats

Marsh Incubators, Gardener Grove, California, CA 92643.
Roll X, Turn X Incubators

Robin Haigh
Distributors for Marsh

David Nickerson (Tathwell) Ltd., North Ormsby, Louth, Lincs. LN11 0TL.
Wormex, Gape Worm Treatment

Brinsea Products Ltd., Knightcott Ind. Est., Banwell, Avon BS24 6JN. *Incubators*

R. H. & B. Moncaster, Fairfield Ind. Est., Louth, Lincoln. *Welded Wire Mesh*

George H. Elt Ltd., Eltex Works, Worcester.
Incubators, Drinkers, Heaters, Feeders, Bins

A. C. Hughes, High Street, Hampton Hill, Middlesex TW12 1NA. *Leg Bands*

Grouse

INDEX OF COMMON NAMES
(in English, Swedish, Norwegian, German and French)

	Species No.	Page No.
Alpenschneehuhn	1.5	54
Auerhoen	1.2	43
Birkhuhn	1.3	47
Blackcock	1.3	47
Blackcock, Caucasian	1.4	51
Black Grouse	1.3	47
Black Grouse, Caucasian	1.4	51
Caille des Blés	6.2	137
Canadian Spruce Grouse	1.9	63
Capercaillie	1.2	43
Capercaillie, Black Billed	1.1	41
Chicken, Prairie	1.15/16	74/76
Chinese Monal	2.13	111
Dalripa	1.3	47
Fazant	4.6	97
Fasan	4.6	97
Faisan de Chasse	4.6	97
Fjallripa	1.3	47
Francolin, Black	5.6	125
Gélinotte des Bois	1.12	69
Grand Tétras	1.2	43
Grouse, Black	1.3	47
Grouse, Blue	1.11	67
Grouse, Hazel	1.12	69
Grouse, Chinese Hazel	1.13	71
Grouse, Severtzov's Hazel	1.13	71
Grouse, Pinnated	1.15/16	74/76
Grouse, Red	1.6	56

	Species No.	Page No.
Grouse, Ruffed	1.14	72
Grouse, Sage	1.18	79
Grouse, Sharptailed	1.17	78
Grouse, Spruce	1.9	63
Grouse, Siberian Spruce	1.10	65
Grouse, Willow	1.8	61
Hazelhen	1.12	69
Hazelhoen	1.12	69
Hazelhuhn	1.12	69
Himalayan Monal	4.12	111
Järpe	1.12	69
Korhoen	1.3	47
Kwartel	6.2	137
Lagopède d'Ecosse	1.6	56
Lagopède des Saules	1.8	61
Lagopède Muet	1.5	54
Moerassneeuwhoen	1.8	61
Moorschneehuhn	1.8	61
Moripa	1.6	56
Orre	1.3	47
Partridge, Barbary	5.3	120
Partridge, Chukar	5.4	121
Partridge, Common	5.7	126
Partridge, Daurian	5.8	129
Partridge, French	5.5	123
Partridge, Grey	5.7	126
Partridge, Hungarian	5.7	126
Partridge, Red Legged	5.5	123
Partridge, Przhevalski's Rock	5.4	121
Partridge, Rock	5.4	121
Partridge, Sand	5.2	119
Partridge, See See	5.1	118
Partridge, Tibetan	5.9	130
Patrijs	5.7	126
Perdix Bartavelle	5.4	121
Perdix Grise	5.7	126
Perdix Rouge	5.5	123
Pheasant Grouse	3.1/2	86
Pheasant, Amherst	4.1	90
Pheasant, Blue Eared	4.5	96

	Species No.	Page No.
Pheasant, Brown Eared	2.4	94
Pheasant, Caucasian	2.6	97
Pheasant, Common	2.6	97
Pheasant, Copper	2.8	104
Pheasant, Chinese Monal	2.13	111
Pheasant, Elliots	2.11	110
Pheasant, Golden	2.2	91
Pheasant, Green	2.7	103
Pheasant, Himalayan Monal	2.12	111
Pheasant, Japanese Green	2.7	103
Pheasant, Koklass	2.15	113
Pheasant, Lady Amherst's	2.1	90
Pheasant, Mikado	2.10	108
Pheasant, Mongolian	2.6	97
Pheasant, Reeves	2.9	106
Pheasant, Ringnecked	2.6	97
Pheasant, Schlaters Monal	2.14	111
Pheasant, White Eared	2.3	93
Ptarmigan, Common	1.5	54
Ptarmigan, Rock	1.5	54
Ptarmigan, White Tailed	1.7	59
Quail, Bobwhite	5.1	135
Quail, Californian	5.3	138
Quail, Common	5.2	137
Quail, Gambels	5.4	140
Quail, Montezuma	5.6	143
Quail, Mountain	5.7	145
Quail, Scaled	5.5	142
Rapphöna	3.7	126
Rebhunn	3.7	126
Rode Patrijs	3.5	123
Rothuhn	3.5	123
Rödhöna	3.5	123
Schotse, Sneeuwhoen	1.6	56
Schottisches Moorschneehuhn	1.6	56
Sclaters Monal	2.14	111
Sneeuwhoen	1.5	54
Snowcock, Altai	6.1	83
Snowcock, Caspian	6.2	83

	Species No.	Page No.
Snowcock, Caucasian	2.3	83
Snowcock, Himalayan	2.4	83
Snowcock, Tibetan	2.5	83
Steenhoen	5.4	121
Steinhuhn	5.4	121
Stenhöna	5.4	121
Tetras Lyre	1.3	47
Tjäder	1.2	43
Turkey, American	7.1	148
Vaktel	6.2	137
Wachtel	6.2	137
Willow Grouse	1.8	61

INDEX OF SCIENTIFIC NAMES

	Page No.
Alectoris barbara	120
Alectoris chukar	121
Alectoris graeca	121
Alectoris magna	121
Alectoris rufa	123
Ammoperdix griseogulavis	118
Ammoperdix heyi	119
Bonasa bonasia	69
Bonasa sewerzowi	71
Bonasa umbellus	72
Callipepla californicus	138
Callipepla squamata	142
Callipepla gambelii	140
Centrocevcus urophasianus	79
Chrysolophus amherstiae	90
Chrysolophus pictus	91
Colinus virginianus	135
Cotornix cotornix	137
Cotornix japonica	137
Crossoptilon auritum	96
Crossoptilon crossoptilon	93
Crossoptilon manchuricum	94
Cyrtonyx montezumae	143
Dendragopus canadensis	63
Dendragopus falcipennis	65
Dendragopus obscurus	67
Francolinus francolinus	125
Lagopus lagopus	61

	Page No.
Lagopus leucurus	59
Lagopus mutus	54
Lagopus scoticus	56
Lophophorus impeyanus	111
Lophophorus iluysii	111
Lophophorus sclateri	111
Lyrurus mlokosiewiczi	51
Lyrurus tetrix	47
Meleagris gallopava	148
Oreortyx pictus	145
Perdix dauuricae	129
Perdix perdix	126
Phasianus colchichus	97
Phasianus versicolor	103
Syrmaticus reevesi	106
Syrmaticus soemmerringii	104
Syrmaticus mikado	108
Syrmaticus ellioti	110
Tetrao mlokoslewiczi	51
Tetrao parvirostris	41
Tetrao tetrix	47
Tetrao urogallus	43
Tetraogallus attaicus	83
Tetraogallus caspius	83
Tetraogallus caucasicus	83
Tetraogallus himalayensis	83
Tetraogallus tibetanus	83
Tetrao phasis obscurus	86
Tetrao phasis szechenyii	86
Tympanuchus cupido	74
Tympanuchus pallidicinctus	76
Tympanuchus phasianellus	78